YOUNG WORDS

D1635570

YOUNG WORDS

*Award-winning entries from the 1990
W H Smith Young Writers' Competition*

MACMILLAN CHILDREN'S BOOKS

First published 1991 by
MACMILLAN CHILDREN'S BOOKS
A division of Macmillan Publishers Limited
London and Basingstoke
Associated companies throughout the world

ISBN 0-333-55559-7

A CIP catalogue record for this book is available
from the British Library

Printed by WBC Print Limited, Bridgend

CONTENTS

Introduction   7

THE CLOCK GOES FORWARD JUST SWING SWING SWING   9

FLICKING BRUSH STROKES ON FLAKING CANVAS   31

CAUGHT IN MEMORY   49

THE ROAD THAT TAKES ME FAR   75

AT MIDNIGHT, IN MOONGLASSES   109

LOSING THE COLD WAR   133

BARBED-WIRE SMILES AND BARBED-WIRE KISSES   161

JUST LIKE MY THOUGHTS LOOKING FOR
SOMEWHERE TO REST . . .   183

Index   205

Advisory Panel of Judges: Ted Hughes (Chairman), Michael Baldwin,
Edward Blishen, Andrew Davies, Penelope Lively and Margaret Marshall.
Preliminary Panel of Judges: Christopher Bantick, Lynn Barclay, Richard
Brookfield, Linda Hoare, Anna Hopewell, Robert Hunter, Barry Maybury,
Timothy Rogers, Betty Rosen, Professor Harold Rosen, Sheila Shannon, Derek
Warner and Anthony Weeks-Pearson.

INTRODUCTION

At the National Theatre last June, accompanied by the writer V. S. Pritchett, I presented the prizes to the winners of the 1990 Young Writers' Competition. Sir Victor, winner of the 1990 W H Smith Literary Award, was delighted to meet the young writers, and it was most enjoyable to bring together two key elements of our Arts Programme – encouragement of young talent and celebration of mature work.

At the Prize-giving, two National Theatre actors, Sandy McDaid and Jeremy Northam, read out some of the winning entries. Everyone listened, utterly absorbed, and we could feel, as Keats did, that 'fine writing is like fine doing, the top thing in the world.'

Fine writing does not just happen, though. Most of us will acknowledge the influence of parents and teachers in turning us into book-lovers. Those writers who grew up in a home full of books and who met enthusiastic encouragement from teachers with a passion for literature, will know how essential this was in fostering their interest. I am sure that the young writers represented in this book will acknowledge their debt to home and school.

We must not forget the judges, too, who spend long hours reading and re-reading, assessing and evaluating work, and travelling long distances for meetings. Their enthusiasm and dedication has served to make the Competition the most exhilarating and highly regarded literary competition for young people today.

There are also the hundreds of young writers whose work is not printed here, but who nevertheless received a certificate of commendation for their work. They should feel proud of their achievement. Their work was studied and discussed in depth and all the judges agreed that it showed promise. Indeed, some of this year's prizewinners originally won commended certificates when they entered the Competition for the first time.

It is very reassuring, at a time when so much public concern is expressed over standards of literacy in the United Kingdom, to read the work in this book. You will find strong individual styles, fluency and evidence of wide reading: they are keen writers because they are enthusiastic readers. Those looking for embryonic Shakespeares, however, will be disappointed. These sixty-three young people are writers for today and their work is required reading if we want to know what will be published in ten years' time. Who knows, one or two of them may turn out to be W H Smith Literary Award-winners of the future.

Sir Simon Hornby
Chairman of the W H Smith Group

THE CLOCK GOES FORWARD JUST SWING SWING SWING

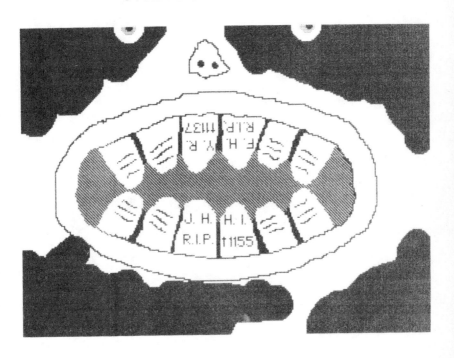

James Hambling (12)

Ansar Yaqoob (11)

MANGO TREE

I will be a mango tree when I grow up,
I will lay some mangoes on my tree
And shout out:
'My mangoes have grown,
Wowee,
Wowee!'
They are beautiful and juicy,
Wowee!
They are lying on my mango machine
As golden balls shining on my face,
It makes me pure gold.
But people snatch my beautiful
mangoes off my beautiful mango tree.
Oh dear mother, what shall I do?
What shall I do?

Sophie Brandram (9)

Miriam Lewis (8)

* **THE MYSTERIOUS EGG**

It was Thursday and Catherine (my friend) and me were walking to school. My teacher had told us to bring something to put on the class nature table. Catherine and me had brought nothing. If we didn't bring anything, Mr Beast our teacher would give us terrible punishments, like the headmaster would never dream of giving a child.

There was a wood next to the infants' school and we went to have a look there, but there was nothing. Partly because of the fact that it was winter, but also because there was a lot of noise coming from the builders who were building the new infants' school.

If the new infants' school wasn't being built, we might have been able to find a snail or a spider or a caterpillar or maybe even a ladybird if we were lucky. I don't know how Mr Beast can expect us to find any nature in the middle of winter!

As we were walking past the infants' school, it was then that Catherine saw the white object.

'Look!' said Catherine. 'Someone's kicked their football in a pit.'

'It's bigger than a football,' I said. 'Let's go and pick it up.' I went over to the pit and reached my hand in. I could feel the white object. It certainly didn't feel like a ball. It felt hard and more like an oval shape. The white object was quite heavy when I tried to lift it. At first I thought I shouldn't be doing this – which was really quite right, because it could be dangerous messing about where there were deep pits.

'Have you got it?' called Catherine.

'Yes,' I called back. 'I don't know what it is but it certainly isn't a ball. It's all hard and egg-shaped.'

I scrambled out of the pit, clutching the mysterious white object tightly in both hands. When I got out of the pit I showed Catherine. Catherine inspected the object carefully as if she was some famous detective.

'I am the great detective Catherine and I have just made an absolutely amazing discovery,' Catherine said after a few moments of looking carefully at the white object.

'Oh yes,' I said, trying not to laugh.

'Oh yes,' said Catherine, looking quite serious. 'I have just found out what this object here in your hand is.'

'What is it then?' I asked. 'A fossilized football or what?'

'No, no, no, my friend, this is . . .' then she hesitated, '. . . this is no football you know.'

'Catherine, just tell me, will you,' I said impatiently.

'This object here in your hands is a giant ostrich's egg!' Catherine said.

'I think you're right,' I said.

Just then the whistle went. It was time to go inside.

In class I showed Mr Beast the egg. He was quite surprised but all he said was, 'That's a big egg you've got there, isn't it,' as if he didn't care if we had found the biggest egg in the world.

I took the egg home that night hoping it would hatch. I wrapped up the egg in my dad's old jumper, put it in a cardboard box and waited. Soon I gave up waiting, had my tea and then went to bed.

Next morning when I woke up I looked in the box. There was the egg. It had a tiny crack in it. There was a slim chance that the egg might hatch the next day.

I told Catherine at school about the egg. Just before I went home I told Mr Beast about it too.

'Mr Beast, you know that egg I showed you yesterday?' I asked.

'Yes?'

'Well I'm going to hatch it.'

'Don't be silly. That was a fossilized ostrich egg,' Mr Beast said loudly.

The next day was Saturday and there was no school. I decided that I would go to Catherine's house, so that she might be able to see the egg hatching with me.

I told my dad where I was going and then I picked up the box with the egg in it and walked to Catherine's house. When I got there I rang the doorbell and Catherine answered the door.

'We have to go to the library to get some books on breeding chickens,' I said to Catherine.

'Breeding chickens?' Catherine asked. 'Why? We haven't even got any!'

I soon persuaded Catherine to come, so she put her coat on and asked for permission to go out, and soon we were on our way to the library.

We soon found some 'How to Breed Chickens' books there and we took one home to Catherine's house.

At Catherine's house I showed Catherine the crack in the egg. Now the crack was longer, but it didn't look as if the egg was going to hatch. Maybe that fat old Mr Beast was right and it was a fossilized egg, but not necessarily an ostrich's egg. It could be a giant crocodile's egg.

We looked through the book and found the bit about how to hatch the eggs. The problem was we needed someone to sit on the egg and that wasn't very comfortable at all. Even if we did sit on it we wouldn't cover all the egg anyway.

After looking through the book again we gave up and put the box with the egg in it down by the radiator and put some of Catherine's Kylie and Jason tapes on.

In the middle of 'Tears on my Pillow', there was a loud crack.

'Is that part of the tape?' I asked Catherine.

'I hope not,' answered Catherine. 'Because if it is I am going to get grounded for sure. Even though they're mine, my mum and dad bought the tape.'

The crack sounded like someone giving someone else a giant kiss, like the sort of noise you hear on cartoons.

Catherine switched off the tape and we waited.

Then we heard wailing noises. Catherine's mum came down to see what all the noise was.

'What's in that box over there by the radiator?' Catherine's mum asked.

'It's a giant egg,' I told her.

'Well, how can a giant egg make so much noise? All the noise is coming from the box,' Catherine's mum said.

'It might have hatched,' Catherine said. 'Maybe that was what the crack was.'

I went over to have a look in the box. The egg *had* hatched. Whatever had been in the egg was still unseen because my dad's jumper was still over it.

I slowly lifted my dad's jumper. I had such a surprise. In the box was not an ostrich's egg, not a giant crocodile's egg, not a baby ostrich, not a baby crocodile, but a D,I,N,O,S,A,U,R DINOSAUR! It was a little baby brontosaurus.

I showed Catherine and her mum the green baby brontosaurus. Catherine said, 'Wow!' and stood there gaping, and her mum fainted. When Catherine's mum recovered she promised not to tell anyone about the dinosaur apart from my mum and dad and Catherine's dad.

We decided that I should take the dinosaur home. We named him Bronto. Next Monday would be a pet's day so we could bring Bronto in. We might be able to give that beastly Mr Beast a bit of a scare.

On Monday I brought Bronto to school in a box. In the afternoon everyone who had brought a pet had to come up to the front and give a talk about it.

There were cats, dogs, rabbits, hamsters, gerbils, mice, rats, guinea-pigs, even a few stick insects. Other children brought in tortoises, fish and lots of birds.

Mr Beast asked us what sort of animal we had. 'A bron-tosaurus,' we answered.

'Miriam Lewis, I have had just about enough of you. Go and stand in the corner!' Mr Beast shouted.

'But it's true,' Catherine said to Mr Beast.

'You go and stand in the other corner over there,' Mr Beast said. 'I'll have a look in the box later,' he said to Catherine.

When everyone had done a talk about their pet if they had one, Mr Beast started embarrassing us.

'Now Miriam and Catherine, after three will you say "I do not believe in dinosaurs." One, two, three,' said Mr Beast as if we were four-year-olds.

'I do not believe in dinosaurs,' we repeated.

That was the really embarrassing part but we soon got our own back.

'Now give me that box, Miriam. What *is* in there anyway?'

Catherine and me just stood in opposite corners of the room smiling.

'I don't know what you're grinning about,' Mr Beast said. 'I might make you eat a worm or two. Then you wouldn't be so happy, would you!'

Mr Beast looked at the box which was moving up and down on his desk. Most of the other children were gig-gling but not Catherine and me. We knew very well Mr Beast *could* make us eat a few worms if he wanted to.

Mr Beast opened the box. Before he could lift Bronto up, Bronto leapt up on Mr Beast's shoulder and bit his ear. Mr Beast went deep red in the face and the rest of the class started to roar with laughter.

'Get this creature off me!' Mr Beast shouted.

'Only on one condition,' I said. 'Say "I believe in dinosaurs."'

'I believe in dinosaurs,' Mr Beast said.

And I think he did.

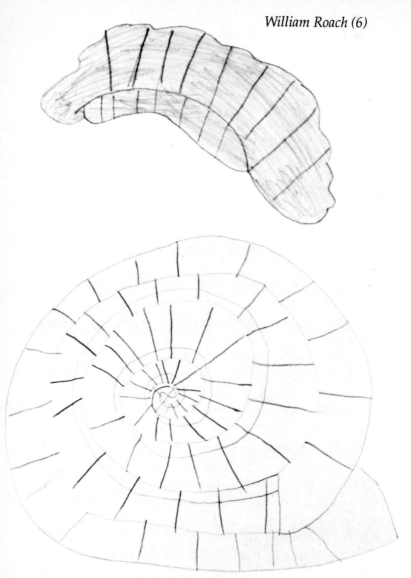

William Roach (6)

Seth Richardson (6)

Katie-Ellen McCrory (6)

FOSSILS

Fossils are flat biscuits
Left behind by untidy picnickers.
There can be lots of biscuits
Like stale jammie doughnuts
That no one wants to eat.

Fossils are animals.
They are snails twirled into a curly ball.
They are worms tucked up,
Snakes slithering in sand.

Fossils are Catherine wheels
Pinned to the sand.
Going round and round in circles,
They throw sparkles out to the night sky.

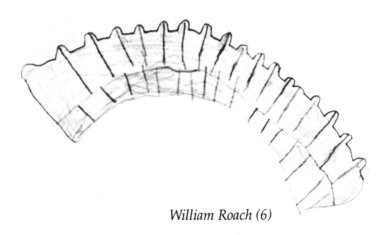

William Roach (6)

Emma Steele-Perkins (11)

* ACORN

O little baby acorn,
Engrossed in your shell,
There is ivy climbing up your tree!

Samannaz Savat-Manesh (8)

Tammy Bird (11)

Marina Plentl (7)

AUTUMN

In autumn I cannot believe my eyes the leaves turn yellow and red. The fresh beautiful airy smell I cannot avoid. I hear my steps go crash crunch. Oh why can't autumn be so long. I like the sound of trees in the wind, so sweet are the animals of this park. I dare not pick the high red mushrooms. The squirrels are the King of autumn. The berries hang glowing bright red and no people seem to run about. But autumn is my lucky season. The fire is bright burning red as night-time falls. I like to sit and tell the tale of autumn falling on the rail. Oh please do not let autumn go. That wicked noise of Hallowe'en. Good-bye pretty blue peck birds but no good-bye to autumn fall. That wicked man can say good-bye by falling down in ashes high. The clock goes forward just swing swing swing. I get up and say it's dark dark dark. I like to dream of autumn season. The people get wrapped up warm in scarves and jackets of soft white wool but I wear more than just one thing. I wear three pairs of woolly white socks. The animals hibernate in small brown nests. I pretend to be a little bird just one step in my nest.

Gavin Goodwin (12)

* **THE WINTER HARE**

The furious blizzard . . .
like my brush
flicking water colour
over the finger-smudged canvas.
But there . . .
    a flash
    a stroke of soft shiny oil.
A hare,
    jumping
    bouncing,
    through the slush,
The slush, like
my mixing tray,
wet and sloppy.

The hare runs
into the hedgerow,
The bare bushes
like a flaking frame.
It stops in the
wet damp leaves . . .

Its little soft nose twitching
like my wet black sponge,
Its whiskers like
some of the finest
bristles out of my stiffest brush.

Its bulging eyes are . . .
like blobs of oil paint
shining and glistening
in the wet winter's light.

Its mouth, a small
smiling mouth,
nibbles at a rotten twig.

Its ears
two finely cut pieces
off an artist's rag,
frayed and smoothed.

But there it sits
a beautifully made animal,
frightened,
starved,
with a future of
death.

Marilyn Rust (12)

Joanna Tyler (13)

* THE MATERNITY WARD

Number 124,
Born 10,
Dead 2.
The maternity ward,
Dung hissing, the bloodstained floor, the piglets
    inside skin,
The sow lies,
In her cot of metal bars,
Rolls of fat, tidal waves,
Underneath, no room for expansion.
A piglet stands in her tiny stiletto shoes,
Her heel stuck through the orange, plastic floor,
A sieve for muck and membrane.
Her mother gently woos her
With soft grunts of wisdom.
The piglet totters for her first found food
To find the wonder of outside and inside combined
The pig's soft skin, gently woven by nature
Into a spider web fleece.
Her skin, the colour of heaven on a sunny day.
A new beginning
Ending for the day to come.
A whirl of blood.
No more.
And the piglet
    sucks on.

*Georgina
Hucker (12)*

Kate Billinge (15)

* MY DAUGHTER

She made me fat and ugly.
She made me sick, and scream.
She made me get stretch marks,
And she made me wear horrible 'Dorothy Perkins'
    clothes,
And that was all before she was born.

I would have preferred a car.
I would have preferred a dog.
I would have preferred a gerbil,
And I would have preferred 'Charlotte',
But no, he wanted 'Tracey'.

Then she reached ten and eleven and twelve.
Then she reached the radio knob.
Then she reached Kylie, Jason and Bros.
And then she tried House, Heavy Metal and Punk.
She settled on Indie. Please help me, God.

I saw her become fifteen.
I saw her become a tarty young woman.
I saw her become a belt mini skirt wearer.
I saw her boyfriend with five earrings.
I would not let him in the house.

I watched her leave home.
I watched her get married.
I watched her become a mother.
I watched her a lot.

I miss her.

Maimuna Chaudry (13)

SCHOOL

The tapping of footsteps
on the lonely cold floor
The moving of the
shadow – from locker to
locker. Walking stealthily
across the slippery
                corridor

The clanking of buckets
The swishing of mops
The sliding of brushes
from classroom to
classroom. And polishing
and wiping of dirty
            desk tops

The bombardment
of boys and the giggling
of girls. As if the whole
world had been tilted
and they were all
swivelling down a
                drain.

Adam Taylor (6)

* THE SILVER LOCKET

It was my first day back at school. I was looking forward to seeing my teacher. I enjoyed doing all her fun projects. Miss walked into the classroom and said, 'This is Philimana, a new girl, who would be joining us this term.'

Philimana looked perfectly normal. What no one knew then was that she could do magic. Philimana was fully aware of her strange power. She did not know where it came from but was quite happy to use it.

I was only five minutes into my space project when she asked to borrow my rubber. I couldn't lend it to her then because I was using it. However, she got angry and exploded into a big belt of words, 'I would shrink your mummy and daddy for this.' I ignored her because whoever heard of real magic in 1990?

When I got home both my parents were fine, so I laughed off the idea of Philimana's words. But my shock was to come next morning. No eggs and bacon on the breakfast table. I shouted, 'Mum! Dad!' but I got no reply. I rushed up to the bedroom, they weren't there. I then heard a little squeak. It was coming from near the pillows. 'Good grief! That rotten girl has shrunk my mum and dad.'

I took them out and took them downstairs. I fed them a few crumbs and placed them gently on the living-room rug. I had to find Philimana quickly. I didn't want to be stuck around with a mother and father this small. Life would be too difficult for me. So I said, 'Goodbye, be careful,' and off to school I went.

I found Philimana in the playground. I was just about to hit her when I thought, if I am horrible to her she might do something even worse to me. I politely said, 'You have made your point, please make my parents normal.'

She looked at me for a moment and then with a little chuckle she said, 'OK.' I asked her how did she do it in the first case. She didn't know. So I said, 'Don't you want to know?' She started to cry, 'Yes I do, yes I do.'

Poor Philimana, I felt sorry for her. 'I don't mean to hurt anyone,' she said. 'When I wish something it just happens, ex . . . except when I am going swimming, please help me.'

So I asked her when it first started. She said it was just after Christmas. So she agreed to sit under the conker tree with me and list all the things that happened and didn't happen. The bell rang and we had to go in but I couldn't stop thinking about this unusual magic power.

It was in the middle of my pin-cushion lesson when the answer came to me. THE SILVER LOCKET. She took the silver locket off that she got for Christmas when she went swimming. So it must be the silver locket.

I couldn't wait for my lesson to finish. 'Philimana!' I said. 'It's your locket.' She looked at me, 'But, but that's a present from my gran.' 'I know, Philimana, but it's the only thing that's different when you wish.' She took it off and handed it to me.

'You try it,' she said. I put it on and said, 'I wish I had an ice-cream,' but nothing happened. 'I never get any really good wishes only my bad wishes better,' she said. So I tried again. 'I wish there was litter in the playground.' Sure enough there were mountains of it everywhere.

'Quickly,' she said, 'Miss is coming, make it better.' I did it just in time. It was Philimana to say the most important thing now. 'We shall just have to lose the locket and soon.'

I looked at her and then I had an idea. I said, 'Locket, locket, I wish you would lose yourself!' It vanished. Philimana and I were very happy. 'You know what,' she said, 'I think you are all right.' I held her hands and we went off to our PE lesson.

FLICKING BRUSH STROKES

ON FLAKING CANVAS

Bilqees Khan (6)

Ryan Payton (8)

* BIRD OF PARADISE

Is like an electric drill
hanging upside down from a branch
with its enormous black beady eyeballs
and its beak has hairs on it
that make him look like he's wearing a false moustache.
And his attractive aqua fur coat with superb
splashes of black ink all over it.
He has gripping claws like a grappling hook
with three inch toe nails.
He sings like a beginner from outer space.

Neil Woolston (12)

Michelle Barnes (12)

* THE PEACOCK

A Japanese fan,
Each feather an old man's eye.
A circular disc of fishy scales,
Splinters of blue glass tinted by the sun,
Oriental colours held in a china vase.
The peacock is the petals fallen from many a flower,
Stuck with morning dew and stitched with spider's web.

This peacock is a Prince riding his white horse,
And wearing a cloak of rainbow.
He swoops away to the maiden's rescue . . .
Then, he is the turquoise sun,
The fire in the sky,
The shimmering haze on a tarmacked road . . .
The Prince arrives and the fanfare plays.
He releases his legs like a vulture to his prey.
Grabbing the ground with onion-ring feet.
And, slowly, he stops and stands tall.
He combs his feathers with fork-like claws.
He stalks on.
A proud and particular creature,
Made into a word.
Beauty in disguise.

Hannah Edwards (12)

* **ROBIN**

The Robin is the creep of the class,
with his discoloured hunched back,
and his small crocheted head,
which holds his close-set compass-point eyes.
When around people you're a gentleman,
a prince of good manners.
But alone you're a bully, pushing and shoving for food.
You're a prison officer, the one that lets nothing pass
   your eye.
You think no one knows
but I saw you through the window.

You have no neck; you're just a lump of clay,
moulded by a three-year-old,
and burnt in the kiln.
You're a tramp,
living in kettles and old broken boxes.
Your legs are knock-kneed, backwards.
Living on other people's mistakes,
and learning from nothing.
Your song is a war dance
and your red breast says,
This is a warning:
red alert
emergency.

Nichola Mason (11)

Sacha Thomas (6)

BLACKBIRD

Black
Little round black eyes.
Sharp yellow beak.
Gripping claws
Shiny black feathers
Light and tricky.
In my garden
Looking for worms.
Hopping about
Head on one side
Listens
Spies
Dives
And swallows.

Hannah Edwards (12)

* THE ANT

The ant is the undertaker of the insect world;
he is the coffin bearer,
he whose black back is shaped like an olive
and whose filtering eyes watch nothing but everything,
everything but himself.
His three-part body is held together with earthing tape
that shines with light and shade
as he advances with his plaque
to a sweet-smelling house,
stealing and carrying off
lumps of apple from a left-over salad;
ants swarm, looking like spots that disappear into a hole
that's nowhere but everywhere.

Gareth Powell-Evans (11)

Stephen Gardam (14)

** FOX

The stream falls away steeply,
Not quite a waterfall.
Roots curve over from its crumbling mud banks,
Twisted arches of the Earth's bone.

He sniffs the air, smelling the dripping leaves,
The stream dribbles quickly by,
Weaving and halting
At fallen branches.
Damp rotten twigs
Flake only slightly under his soft weight.
He feels the damp Earth between his toes,
Delicately picking his way through
The scattered pebbles;
Stumbling only once.

Downstream, the foundations of a tree
Have been gutted by rain and wind;
And the tree rests across the water,
One sinewy branch hanging, bending against the rush.
He flits up the bank,
His steps flicking brush strokes
On flaking canvas.
He reaches out his paw to the mossy log,
And they go hand in hand.

Cautiously he edges out on to the log;
Tail raised for balance.
One of his first few steps slips
On the thin wet moss.

It starts to rain, heavily;
His fur is drenched, and is stood on its end,
Clustered in little spikes.
His tail comes down,
On line with his back, it bristles, the white tip darkening.
The rain washes away his caution,
As he runs lightly across,
And up the crumbling, sodden bank,
Off through the trees, to the holt,
Churning the wet pine needles,
Leaving the bare earth to the patchy sky.
And through the trees, to his left,
The fiord is painted grey by the rain.

Natalie Ward (11)

Victoria Clements (8)

A SLEEKY FOX

I am a sleeky fox,
Living in an old badger's sett,
I run through dark velvet night
Underneath the stars.

I eat a rabbit or two,
Then run on to eat other things,
I am the night king.

I've got beady eyes
To find food with,
And two good ears for
the same purpose.

Louise Noller (12)

Emma Buckingham (12)

* **COWS**

Two idle cows lurched in the field . . .
Two lost pieces of a chess set, placed there on purpose,
Their tails mopping
The field of its ploughed crust.
A jewel of perspiration hung on one cow's nose
And saliva drooled in steamy strings.
Four glaring eyes,
On the brink of an inquisition,
Began to prepare for battle.
The cow's teeth were an exact image . . .
Of a row of tombstones, grass-stained
And chipped at the corners.
Tripping over the field
The milk-filled bellies of the cows tossed wildly
As they came to meet us,
Grinning with an overpowering welcome.
We turned and walked away.

Our back to two lost pieces of a chess-set
Placed there on purpose.

Catherine Clarke (12)

OUR DEN

A sachet of spider's eggs
Hangs by an umbilical thread
From a rusted metal bar in
The gloom.

The sun filters through whispering
Branches, that poke and prick
Like wooden needles that sew
The air.

Tangling, strangling ivy overruns
Churned, sodden soil and drowns
Other life forms hibernating in
Our garden.

Crouching in aching silence,
Secrecy claims our itching limbs
Hiding from ants that Gestapo patrol
Our den.

Protected in a fantasy world,
The green film of leaves keeps us unknown,
As we fold like wet cardboard in our den –
Our secret bubble.

Catherine Clarke (12)

Clare Broderick (6)

TOMATOES

The tomatoes are squashy and it looks tasty but I am not going to have a bite. It is shiny and the spider part is hairy and it is very dark green. It is very curly and the tomato is smooth. The splits are like a star and it is cold and it is red. It is a shady red and it is like a squashy ball. It is fat and it is bumpy it smells like a dustbin. On the top of the tomatoes it looks like a wand sparkling and it was.

Lorraine Beresford (8)

JAPANESE BRIDGE

The bridge is like a mouth
With water in it.
It looks like it's just about
To swallow the water.

When a duck swims through
It looks like it's taken a tablet,
A multi-coloured one.

Helen Felcey (11)

CAUGHT IN MEMORY

Elisa Hudson (18)

Bilqees Khan (6)

* THE SWAN

One day, I went to the park and I saw some swans in the lake. They were swimming in the water. They were white and they had a beak. It was early in the daytime. The sunshine was making the swans look golden and the water twinkle. When the swans were swimming they made waves in the lake. Sometimes the swans used their necks to put their beaks in the water to get a drink. They moved slowly and carefully. That was their motion and it seemed gentle to me. It made my heart feel happy.

Anoushka Seneviratne (7)

Michelle Barnes (12)

* THE TADPOLE IS . . .

A priest,
Swimming amongst his congregation,
And wearing a rough robe of black
As he preaches to the shimmering stickleback.
The tadpole . . .
So soft, but so swift, and speedy, and slick.
The tadpole is an ink smudge
Spilt from the finest of pens.
It quavers like a shrill note,
Then stiffens to that one pose.
The tadpole is a stowaway.
Hiding.
Evacuating from its every home.
No safe place to hide for the tadpole.

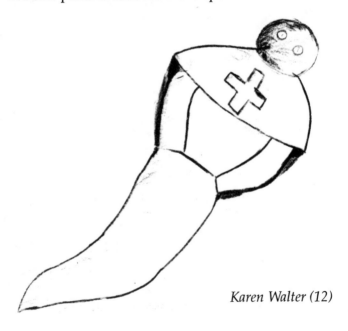

Karen Walter (12)

Evan Brown (9)

Evan Brown (9)

* **MACKEREL**

Sliding through my fingers,
Machine-like fins beating
Against my hand.
Its pearly eyes meeting mine,
I looked into them
And saw the bewildered gaze.
For a moment its bluey-green back
Quivered,
And I put it in the basket.
But when I started eating,
All the sorrow
Melted with the butter.

Avril Huston (14)

** SEA SWIMMING

Kicking into the water –
A sharp, gasping ecstasy of cold brine
Striking ankles.
Gentle slope of muscles
Nearing the sea and finally hitting
La Manche – denim-blue sleeve
Buttoning Britain to the Continent.
Prickling pain in the joints
Coming from sheer chill,
Then release. The sun flings
Yellow on the surface of the sea
As the swimmers grin and shriek and splash,
Gliding with neat co-ordination,
Riding the waves.
I feel that there will never be long enough
To stay in the sea forever. I need to be
Just one of the lives that is spent in the water, alone.
I want to be a dolphin, a curved strip of pure
Muscle, arching above the wrinkled sea,
Plunging deep to the saline bed.
Leaving the water, stepping onto powdery French sand
I miss the sea. A fantasy of a million dolphins crumbles
Left behind, on the beach, like an abandoned sandcastle.

Lorna Davies (14)

Rebecca Prochnik (16)

* **BALLET**

Clad in chequered table-cloth
Skirt, and elastic
Bites
Hungrily, my baby flesh.
The chill of the icy corridor freezes
Through my nylon leotard. I lean, I balance,
I struggle. Forcing on my pumps of pink
Leather: three pound ninety-seven from Woolies.
Uncombed hair straggles
Escaping its hasty arrangement.

Says the painted lady of the peroxide bottle,
'Nadine et Pascale, allez tout de suite!'
'Oui, Maman' in unison.
Dark, cherub curls pinned elegantly
Nadine folds to the ground,
The dying swan
Her face, so intent and severe
As she fastens a silken ribbon
About her fair ankle.

Daintily, how daintily
They arabesque
And sweep across the wooden hall.
Mothers watch,
Proud and alert, an attentive audience.
My father waits
Exhausted and bored, thinking of supper.
His eyes rest, secured
Upon the ticking clock.

'And bend!' She patrols up and down
Her watchful gaze rests dissatisfied
As I desperately, failingly attempt a plié.
She taps my stomach instructively
'Belly in!' I flush a humiliated vermilion.
That isn't belly, it's fat, I answer bitterly
In
My
Head.

Old Mrs Grindely plonks,
Deafly, on the piano.
And I falter and plunge
Awkward, as I jeté and sauté and mournfully
Envy their slim structures
Until quarter to seven.

'All right, girls, well done and see you next week.'
Not I, I think gratefully. An evil smile
Spreads across my lips as I rip
The hateful slippers
From my feet and drown them mercilessly
In
The Waiting
Toilet. I watch them gasp and suffocate.

My father and I slip away into the night,
Freed forever.

Anthony Graham (10)

* **IT'S IMPOSSIBLE**

This was the hardest thing
that I had to do in my
life. I had to tell my
brothers and sisters that
our Grandfather, the only
Grandfather we had, was
dead. I walked slower every
minute to try and avoid
it but this was a thing
I had to do by myself.
Eventually my house came
into sight and there
outside it were my
brothers and sisters. I
lingered around the house
for ten minutes thinking
what way I would tell
them the bad news, every
minute wondering should
I go through with this
or turn back. Eventually
I plucked up enough courage
to call them over and
blurt out the words
'Granda's dead'.
They all bursted out crying
the very second I told them
and I began to feel it was
me who had made them cry.
Ever since that day I can say
any hard thing imaginable.

Marina Plentl (7)

GRANDAD

Grandad smelled of fish boiled in milk
And liquorice root on which he continuously chewed,
Grumbling about taking pills,
Although they were all that kept him alive.

There was a pile of pipe cleaners
By the fireplace
Smelling of dust
And used too many times,
Like the bleached chicken bones
On the birdtable.

He had been working on the allotment
In his better trousers
So they got muddy
And he had scrubbed them
With a wire brush.
Then had to try and darn them again.

The hardened globule of denture cream
Looked like birdsplash
On the side of the vase,
In which flowers melted into the water,
Staining the glass at the waterline.

When I was very small
There was always a toy phone
On which we played a game
In which he ordered sacks of potatoes.
So I used to bring them round,
Out of the garage.
He gave me 5 pence per sack.

Then he died,
Mixing with smells
Of camomile tea
And boiled fish.

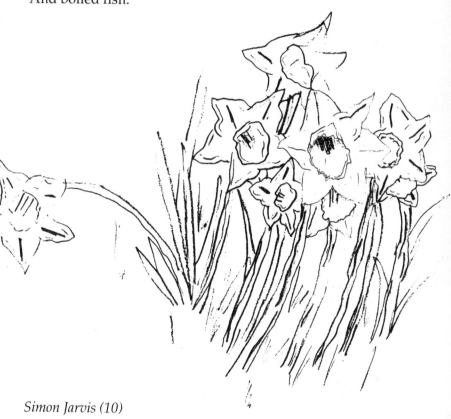

Simon Jarvis (10)

Stephen Gardam (14)

** THE TIME OF DAY

A tiny, near-bald rat,
Out of a sun-coloured mother.
He grew, suckling milk as warm and rich
As compost.
A knock-kneed puppy,
One ear tumbled over his eye,
Like a stubborn forelock.
His fur was imitation gold velvet,
The gold at the fringe
Of a fresh sun-risen autumn stream.
It is morning.

He has grown,
His legs have straightened,
His coat has mellowed,
His muscles ripple as water-filled balloons
As he leaps, the blue and green ball
Caught.
In memory
As he comes to earth
The sun has climbed; it is noon.

He will tire,
The balloons will burst,
And the water drained away.
The blue and green ball
Will wear thin, and rot from damp.
The light from his sun-coloured mother
Will have been extinguished long ago.
He will lie in front of a new fire,
Lapping cold, treated milk,

As hollow to taste
As licking Christmas envelopes for the world.
And his coat will lose its shine,
Grow unfocused,
The halo of a summer sunset
In the late evening.

And his face will wrinkle,
His sight will blur,
Eyes trying to look through seawater.
The new-born kitten,
Trying vainly to pump blood through his ancient body

Will give up, tired of work,
And he will die.
For the Sun-dog's coat will shine no more;
For one day all stars will die,
And there will be eternal night.

Stephen Gardam (14)

Helen Semple (12)

* THE DEATH OF ANTHONY

My mind rose from sleep with the same anxiety of the previous evening still foremost in my thoughts. In a moment I had risen and softly crossed to the opposite side of the room, and the cage which stood pressed close to the suffocating heat of a radiator at full blast. As I drew nearer my heart lurched and a lump rose in my throat as I saw the untouched dish of carefully prepared egg food and the still, sock-wrapped bundle within. And as I unwrapped the soft woollen sock with which I had cushioned Anthony's last evening, there was no doubt. He was dead.

It had all started with the purchase of three white Fan-tailed doves – Caesar being the male – thus fulfilling my childhood dream of owning white doves. However, I thought that an odd number of birds was not a good idea, and began to search around for an aviary that would sell us another male. Eventually we found what seemed to be the answer. Yes, they had a male dove, and yes, it was white, but whoever it was sounded a bit hesitant. After well over half the day spent driving out into the backwaters of Kent (aviaries are nearly always in the backwaters of Kent) we arrived and were shown to a small aviary. There, sitting soberly on a perch with a few raucous parakeets, was a solitary white dove.

I took a closer look. Yes, it was certainly a white dove, with the most elegant head and pair of shoulders I had ever seen, but there was something else. It was a great deal smaller than my three Fan-tails (which are, roughly, the size and build of a large feral pigeon) and also, the whole stance was different, with the bird sitting straight upwards, still as attractive as the Fan-tails, but in a different way. To be frank, I had my doubts.

As Cassius (as we decided to call him – Shakespeare's play *Julius Caesar*: 'Cassius has a lean and hungry look . . .') failed to grow or mate with either female, we came to the conclusion that he must be another species. After much research, we found that he was a Java dove, meant to be kept in aviaries since they, unlike pigeons and Fan-tails, have no homing instinct. At this point I hastily put in a dish of the recommended millet seed rather than the coarse pigeon food, and Cassius became noticeably sleeker and fatter.

A few months later, Dad bought me a splendid dovecote which he bolted to the wall. The end of six months' patient waiting was drawing close, and soon we could let the doves fly free, only returning to the dovecote to sleep. Cassius and his young mate, Calpernia, would live in the proposed aviary with my small (but growing) colony of Zebra Finches. Then came the evening when Dad and I transferred three struggling white bundles to the roomy dovecote and went inside, full of hope.

The next morning my three white Fan-tails, Caesar, Crystal and Pearl, whom I had protected and fed for half a year, flew off to live with the feral pigeons on a nearby apartment block, never to return to our garden.

During the Easter holidays of the same year, when I was beginning to make preparations for secondary school, the aviary began to take shape, and in the last week before the beginning of term, we moved Cassius, Calpernia and their young daughter Cleopatra into the newly built complex which was to be their home. At first, all was well. We found a home for Cleopatra with a neighbour, and for one of the next brood, who were called Romulus and Remus. So we were back to the original total of three doves in a fairly large aviary and peace seemed to reign. The end of the summer term was near when a new complication arose.

The pair were sitting on a pair of young chicks, and I

had already named them, the older one Octavius, the younger one Anthony. However, I was asked by my drama teacher if I could use Calpernia as my familiar in the end-of-term play (I was a prophet) and somewhat foolishly, I agreed. I knew that Cassius did most of the rearing of the chicks and I assumed he could do without his mate for a few days. So, for nearly every day for well over a week, Calpernia was taken to school for practice. She was a docile, obedient bird (and still is!) and she was kept backstage so that she was not alarmed by any sudden movements (one such incident had already had me climbing into the rafters) so I do not think this was too much of a trauma for her, but Cassius was frantic and spent most of the days searching for his mate. When she returned, he was calmed, but the damage was done. Cassius became over-protective of her and hostile to his not-so-young son Remus, who was becoming a fine young dove. After one scuffle, Cassius lost his temper and stabbed with his beak (for a dove, Java doves' beaks are surprisingly sharp!) at a Zebra Finch perching innocently beside him. I removed him to his cage, which was very long (much longer than my arm) and then retired.

The next morning I rose and went to check on the birds, and saw to my horror that Cassius's feathers were blood-stained, and there were flecks of crimson on the floor. I immediately resolved to take Cassius into the house to see how serious his injuries were.

The cage was sitting on a pile of junk in the old wood-shed, with a wall on three sides. When I opened the door, Cassius immediately retreated to the end of the cage, and I was unable to catch him. Finally I lost my temper, and thrust my entire arm and shoulder through the door, lowering my head and thus creating a small gap. The next I knew was a familiar faint hooting sound as white wings actually brushed my ear and Cassius shot through the gap and onto a nearby tree.

Freddie Bryant (12)

As every bird keeper knows, escape for aviary birds is almost invariably death.

I was not shown his body.

Some weeks later, I was making polite conversation at a dinner party, something I loathe, and fairly soon I found a plausible excuse and excused myself from the stuffy room. Released, I went outside for a breath of fresh air and it occurred to me that it might be a good idea to start hand-training Anthony, who was now fairly well-developed, though still entirely dependent on his mother for food. I opened the insulated breeding compartment and all thoughts of training instantly vanished from my mind as I saw the small sad bundle which had been a healthy dove. As I rushed him indoors and saw the loose skin over bones I knew immediately what had happened. Distressed by the death of her mate and unable to cope with a duty suddenly thrust upon her, Calpernia had not been feeding her son, and he was near death. After an exhaustive evening driven mad with worry and developing new skills as I tried to force the young bird to live, I found my efforts had been in vain. It was probably shock in the end.

I have seen many deaths since that time in my aviary, but none has affected me as much as the death of Anthony. His brother, Octavius, only a week older, is now mature and I cannot help thinking how much difference a little time can make.

NOTE: I would like to make it clear that all of the above is completely, utterly and totally true.

Anya Haworth (11)

Philip Robinson (15)

THE CRASH

I was disturbed from my semi-conscious trance by a sharp pain which snaked up my arm to my neck. I was flung backwards and then forwards in a moment. As I tried to recover myself, I glanced at the windscreen. No more was it a transparent, smooth sheet of shiny glass. It had metamorphosed into an opaque, cruelly toothed monster sitting between the bonnet of the car and the roof.

I shifted my gaze to the rear-view mirror. My face was untouched except for a trickle of blood which wound its way from my nose to my top lip. My eyes suddenly fell on the shape on the back seat next to me like a vulture upon carrion. It was my father. He was hunched over, face downwards. My first thought was to lift his upper body into an upright position. Then I was struck by a thought so sharply that I almost gasped. If I made any effort to move his crouched form, I could make worse any injury that he may have.

The voice of a stranger told me to get out of the car. I had no real idea what was going on so I simply complied with what I was ordered to do.

As I stepped out into the warm summer day, I realised that I was standing like a zombie in the fast lane of a motorway. Thoughts crashed around in my mind like a whirlwind as I attempted to register all that had happened. My feet were ensnared by a field of evil daggers of glass and I had to tread as would a soldier in a mine field.

Total strangers became concerned with my welfare as I was asked on a number of occasions if I was all right. After being shepherded to the grass at the roadside, I was joined by my mother and youngest sister. Apart from their obviously distraught state, I could see nothing physically wrong with them.

The friendly, concerned face of a middle-aged woman appeared before me as if I had switched on a television. She began telling me that her son was a doctor and was going to do all that he could. I looked down and saw that my hands were spotted with blood because I had used them to remove the blood from my nose.

When the woman saw them, the balance of friendliness and concern on her face shifted to almost all concern. Clockwork clones in crisp, clean uniforms had arrived by now. I was only able to differentiate between them when they approached me. The woman called one, a calm-looking man, over to see me.

It was not until he had inspected my hands closely that the mistake was realised. The three of us managed a shallow laugh which was quickly dispelled when I saw the car. It was crumpled and diminished as if someone had attempted to squeeze it into a small box.

I looked around for the other car that had been involved in the accident but could find nothing. Next to me was a lamp-post that appeared to have been kicked by an enraged elephant. It leaned backwards and its base had been uprooted from the concrete.

All around us lay a bright red jigsaw which used to be our car. Pieces of it even sprawled up the hill behind us. A silly thought crossed my mind, 'Can I remember my name?'

I proceeded to go through my name and address in my head to see if there was suffering from amnesia. Almost to my disappointment I found that I could remember everything.

By now, the motorway looked like a crazy battlefield; sirens blazing like machine guns; lights flashing all round; and manic manikins scuttling everywhere. Yet another uniformed troop, this time a young lady, approached and told me that she worked for the St John's Ambulance Service. Again I was asked if I was all right, and it seemed to me that I had been asked nothing else in my life.

An older male, whose profession was given away by his oddly shaped, canary-yellow hat, began to talk to the woman and the menagerie of sound grew to an horrific tumult. I do not know if my mind was refusing to understand what was being said but the only words that I kept hearing were, 'Father in the back,' and 'Teenager still inside.'

This was the first moment that I realised that my father and older sister had not joined us at the roadside. Thoughts flashed through my brain, turning like a carousel, until my mind returned to the present scene.

I looked again at the uncomforting face of the strange lady and asked her if my father and sister were all right. Her voice, quiet, stern and definitely Northern, told me that my father was already inside one of the many ambulances and that my sister was to be cut out of the car like some diseased growth inside a body. I could still not really focus anything in my mind and so this did not mean very much to me.

I looked up at the bridge in the gods of this mad theatre and saw a large crowd peering down, watching the scene that was like a BBC drama. Shouts were floating around me and one of these wraith-like voices told us to follow the man in the blue uniform into the ambulance.

Bleak-looking stretchers were provided for my sister and mother, but I had to walk. I was ushered into an ambulance which had an interior very similar to the small bus that runs past our home. The vehicle was empty until a robust man, who wore a jacket that would have brightened a church, jumped in. He told me to climb on to the waiting stretcher. I told the man that I didn't need it, but he almost pushed me on to it.

I found it rather embarrassing to be wheeled across the

motorway into yet another semi-luminous health vehicle, where I found my mother and sister. The doors at the back crashed shut and the man leapt into the driver's seat. The large vehicle roared into action and we were soon tearing down the road. Only one thing was on my mind, 'Where am I going?'

THE ROAD THAT TAKES ME FAR

Alison Rawlings (12)

Kate Beckinsale (16)

** TWO ROADS

Come away, come away, death,
And in sad cypress let me be laid.
Fly away, fly away, breath,
I am slain by a fair cruel maid.
  My shroud of white, stuck all with yew,
    O! Prepare it;
  My part of death, no one so true
    Did share it.

Not a flower, not a flower sweet,
On my black coffin let there be strown,
Not a friend, not a friend greet
My poor corse, where my bones shall be thrown;
  A thousand, a thousand sighs to save,
    Lay me O! where
  Sad true lover never find my grave,
    To weep there.

(William Shakespeare, *Twelfth Night*)

As I was parking the car on the glassy sidewalk, I noticed my breath fogging out in great gobs from my mouth, fat and smoking like an expensive cigar. It was a cold night. I leaned forward with my tweed arms over the wheel, and saw the cold road with all its dying-soldier trees stretching out like a promise. The lights were out in the house, except for two; one above, one below. Before I knocked on the door, before I even pushed open the chipping black-painted gate, I stood in the middle of the street, with the cardboard apartments stacking up behind me the colour mushrooms, and I stared for a while. It was a tall house, skinny, and with surprised-looking gabled windows, that glared down archly, like three pairs of eyes; and past one I saw the stooped figure of my father bend itself into a sit. The street was so still I could almost hear my heart and my blood, greedily blowing through my body and my head, and my ears rang with a sullen thump that came muffled from inside my throat.

'Push me, push me.'

My father opened the door, and with a grey face, and grey sweatered arms, he buried me into an awkward hug.

I looked around, and saw that nothing had changed. It had been almost five years since I'd set foot inside the house, and the same old smell of coats hung pockety and cold in the hallway, and the squares of glass that had fallen out of the pattern in the window were still missing.

'Before you go up,' said my father, already reaching for a cigarette, and sitting down in one of the pale kitchen chairs, 'I thought we could have a little talk.' He puffed out smoke and sighed from inside his belly. 'It's been a long time.'

'Yes it has,' I found myself saying. 'A long time.'

He was the black-shirted priest at the altar and I was the whole congregation, mumbling the standard litany that he fired from within his robes. My mother was upstairs, the sacrificial lamb, ready to be slit at the throat.

'And we've missed you. Both of us. I'm sorry to bring you away from your life like this, but she did say specially . . . '

'It's all right, Dad, I understand.'

Understand? I didn't know anything any more. One minute I was sitting in my own house with my own books stacked round me keeping the demons out, and the next, here I was, back Home. It felt strangely hollow.

My father reached up to the third shelf where the tea was kept in a Coronation tin and began boiling the kettle, setting out a little tray, milk, sugar, cups and saucers and langues de chat on a flowered plate. I looked out of the back-door screen window again. I could see the old wooden fence that made the yard our yard, and the chimney-grey of the rooftops piling high behind it. The road was a long one, and a twisted one. It forked at the end, one fork lined with poplars, and the children on bicycles, and the other one empty and old, and the nearest thing our suburb had to a slum. I'd spent so long sitting at the fork looking into the dust-hole. It was a place my mother had never been.

'You look so much better,' said my father, almost ready to pour the tea and mashing his cigarette into a fish-shaped ashtray. Burn it, I thought; burn it right to its gills and hear it screaming from its no-throat depths.

'Thank you.'

He brought the tray to the table and sat. I felt if I took any more liquid I'd suddenly become all wet and watery, starting at my feet; and then disappear down the plug, down the drain, and under the earth in a great, green sludgy puddle.

He plinked milk, by drops, into his own cup, and then into mine.

'Push me, push me.' I was starting to feel a little faint.

I pushed the tea a little way away from me. Just looking into its peach-brown wetness made me feel strange.

'I think I'll go straight up,' I said.

My father smiled. 'Good girl.'

I climbed the stairs, passing my old room, and my old bed with its bare walls and cracked basin, and before I went into my mother's room, I stopped and sat down on my own bedroom floor. It smelled stuffy, even though it was cold and I leaned over to the window, and looked out at the flat roof. I could see the fork from there. One side lit, the other in an orange-pinky darkness with shadows thrown on the road and no lights in the houses.

I stopped on the third step before my mother's room.

I could smell a yellow, chickeny smell drifting under the door, and I could hear the old green lamp buzzing, as it always had, and right then and there I was just about ready to take to my legs and hurtle down the brown stairs and out the front door into the street, where it was safe and clear and quiet.

I opened light into her room from the landing.

'Mother?' It took me a few seconds to adjust to the halflight where she was lying. She sat up, small as a newt in the rumpled, muddy ocean that was her bed. I went over and lumped down beside her. The smell was so strong. Smell of roses. Smell of canker.

'Push me, push me, push me.'

She looked so old. It had only been five years, and she was like an old woman. For the first time in my life I had nothing at all to say. I just looked and looked, and felt heady from that terrible yellow smell, and I could feel myself beginning to sweat under my clothes. I still hadn't taken off my coat.

'You look beautiful,' she said.

'Thank you.'

'Kate, I wanted you here. There are some things I can't leave to your father. I needed my girl back.'

She let a thin tear pearl out of her eye and spiral down to her chin.

'I've missed you so much.'

I nodded. 'Me too.'

This was crazy. We were almost strangers again. All that time when I'd been like a part of her body, when I had to tell her everything in case she died and left me with a guilty secret like a pavement slab dragging me down to hell by my stupid turkey neck; when I'd half-way walked the dingy fork, even though I was afraid, in that terrible March wind, and had belly-aches from the guilt I felt when I came drooping back, too plumbed up with fear to continue.

'Lord, keep her safe this night.'

I felt like shaking her by her muley shoulders until the whole rotten worm that was eating inside her belly flew out of her mouth with a ping-pong ball pop, and she'd be well.

'Now listen to me,' she said, 'just sit and listen and then forget you ever came and had to see me in this stupid mess.'

She was almost ashamed of dying. My perfect mother had tripped over and fallen into a dirty old ditch with her long white legs in the air and all the world staring down.

'I want to be wearing the grey silk dress with those nice sleeves all buttoned at the wrist,' she was saying, 'and those silver ankle strap shoes I have. They're in blue tissue at the back of the cupboard.'

I stared, almost goggling.

'Put the diamond clip thing in at the back, and the tulip brooch on the left hand side. I'll keep my rings on . . . unless you want them?'

I shook my head.

O! Silver lady with your rotting belly, I thought, I'll bury you in your dove silk and your diamond dancing shoes. I'll make you beautiful again.

'Make sure it's clean,' my mother was saying. She wiped spit from her mouth with a crumpled tissue.

'You'll find the stockings in that drawer,' she pointed. 'Silver birch nylon. Straight seams, now!'

She laughed and shook her head. 'Well, I guess that's it,' she said. 'Just leave these earrings in, they'll do, won't they?' She pulled back a twist of hair and I saw silver roses on her earlobes.

'They'll do fine,' I said.

'Right.'

I could hear the lamp buzz more than ever, and the old clock clucked thick thumps out into the stairwell.

'Push me, push me.'

81

'Well,' she said. 'It's lovely to see you again. How have you been?'

'Oh fine, you know. Too much coffee, too little sleep.'

I hated myself and my chirpy city voice that cracked and withered as soon as it leapt from my mouth.

I wanted to pick her up like a bird and put her into my car for one last drive. She'd never been before, though, and she wouldn't go now.

'Just you take care, now. Look after yourself. Meet people – have some fun.' She was nodding earnestly. I could hardly speak.

And then the nodding was faster and she clenched up monkey-fists and a yellow phlegm coughed out of her mouth and into my hands and she was screaming, hellcat, hellfire, breathing out her yellow smell and her body bent double with the stabbing that came from inside; Hecate's own black dove, white raven; and I was running, suddenly, hurtling down the brown stairs screaming for my father, and out the front door and into the street, and the light buzzed still in my ears, and her pain was all over my hands; egg-yolk rat-slime stickier than glue.

'Push me, push me,' I was screaming in a voice I hardly knew, like a fallen jackdaw, and it all stuck sharp, suddenly in my throat, and I was lying in the street with my hair in the gutter, and the heat from my breath was wet on my lips. I drove away into the coldness and the haze of early winter evenings.

'Lord, keep her safe this night.'

The silver dove sparkled in her yellow nest; and the soft chattering of her mate fell like dirty rain on to the dullness, deafness, of her shining, rose-flower ears.

'Push me, push me, push me.'

As I parked the car on the sidewalk, I noticed the stillness and the silence, and the cold, cold emptiness of my own forked road, that stretched out before me if only I would walk it.

John Westell (8)

Ashley Starkey (15)

* **WOODEND LANE**

In the back streets of my town
the kids all scream an' shout
Hey mister go home you Don't
wanna stay 'ere.
But I just keep walkin' on.

The headlights of cars shine in
the eyes of passers-by like
the oval shapes of glowing coals
in a fire. But I keep walking on.

I come to a sign that I can't
quite make out
A kid rides past and shouts
I'd get out of here cause this is Woodend Lane.
I keep on walking in the dark
and I keep on walking on.

The trees all looming above my head,
telling me to turn back
From Woodend Lane
with their rustling, whispering voices
But I keep on walking on.

The street lights fight back the darkness
and here a noise,
a cat that's been rummaging
in trash cans at the Chinky.
But I keep on walking on
But I keep on walkin' on.

John Howden (8)

*   **DRIFT WOOD**

Elephant skin all wrinkly.
Smooth dry sides of bones in a cave.
Wavy corners carved by breaking waves.
Hard bumpy skunks nose smelling the air.
Gloomy, black like the starless night
Deep caves leading to the heart of you.

Anna Mitchell (5)

* **OVER THE ROAD**

Looking over the road
I can see the terraced houses.
They look like five sad faces
Looking at me.
The bedroom windows
Are like half-closed eyes
With their net curtains hanging down.
The tiled porch
Is like a nose.
The closed door
Is like a silent mouth.
The rain drops down
From the shiny rooves
And the houses
Look as if they are crying
Big sad tears.

Dylan Ferley (10)

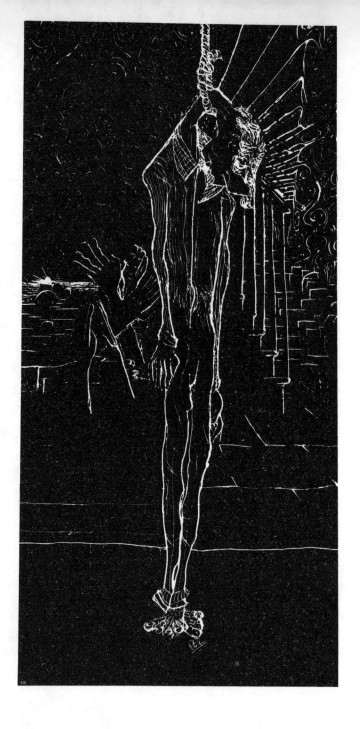

Tom Ellis (17)

Andrew McNaught (16)

*   **THE HANGING**

The gallows was made of old wood,
With wet steps
Like the steps up to the doctor's surgery
That I went to with my son.

I slipped climbing up the steps,
And was grabbed from behind by two warders.
Their hands felt like my mother's,
Catching me when I fell as a baby.

As the mask came over my head
The noise quietened,
Like the lasso going round the colt's head,
Ending its freedom.

REFLECTIONS

A nurse hurried into the room and bustled about noisily, but then stopped and crept out quietly. She obviously thought that Joanna, lying inert and silent on the bed with her eyes firmly shut, was asleep. The girl was relieved; her calm outward appearance belied an emotional, frantic mind. The questions that had bombarded her mind for so long continued to do so, and she could find no answers. Uppermost was, 'Why me? Why at all?' It seemed so silly. She had known about it for quite a while, and she should have come to terms with it by now, but she could not accept it, that she had to be the one out of all the girls at school, to get a brain tumour.

She used to believe in God. She had gone to the local church every Sunday, and, when she remembered, she would say a prayer at night. She had told her friends that she didn't really believe in God, that she had done it to please her Grandmother; but she had always had a vague belief in God – something had to be in control, she had thought. And now this had happened. If anything could be so severe as to destroy a person's religious beliefs it would be a disease like this. One where you could go on to the operating table and not come out alive. And if you did come out alive you could be so severely mentally handicapped as to be classified as a 'vegetable'. Joanna shuddered involuntarily. That was too awful to contemplate. Of course there was another possibility: the operation might not succeed and another would be required. Even if it was successful it might already have been too late; if the tumour was medulloblastoma, that is malignant, it might have spread to other parts of her body before anything could be done, and she might be condemned to years more of interminable hospital visits such as this.

She thought back. It had only started about a year ago – but it seemed like ten. She had developed an unsteady gait: she just could not seem to walk any distance without losing her balance. She had previously been a keen athlete, but that had all ended when she became progressively worse, and eventually broke her leg on the hurdles, and could no longer face the humiliation of falling over in every race and invariably coming last. The teachers had shown no sympathy: some said that it was 'just a phase' – but then some said that to everything. Others seemed to think she was doing it on purpose, in order to try to miss games lessons. The fact that she loved games seemed to them to be entirely irrelevant. Even her parents seemed doubtful about it, and it wasn't until she fractured her leg that they decided to have tests carried out at the local hospital.

After exhaustive x-rays, blood tests and scans, they came to a final conclusion: she had a brain tumour.

She remembered wryly the silence that had followed the specialist's diagnosis, and prognosis. None were remotely prepared for such news: her parents had persuaded themselves that it was nothing serious, that it was just a part of the growing up cycle: normal changes that had affected her particular body. It would soon pass, they had thought to themselves, it's not important.

And none of them had even known exactly what it meant – it had taken nearly an hour of careful explanation by the doctor, with many emotional, even hysterical out-bursts from both her parents and Joanna herself, to convince them all that she might not die, that everything might be all right, so long as action was taken fast. They were going to have to drill a hole in her head and fish the offending object out.

Her mother would not look her directly in the eye when they had left. And Joanna had seen a tear escape and run down her mother's cheek, before being hastily brushed away.

It was strange. Joanna herself had felt oddly detached from it all, as if it wasn't really anything to do with her, as if all the commotion would die down soon, so that life could return to normal.

That was two weeks ago.

Her parents were due in half an hour. They had come yesterday, and of course the day before when she had signed into the hospital. Yesterday they had brought chocolates and flowers, but the chocolates had been taken away by a nurse because she was 'Nil by Mouth' until the operation, which was to take place in one hour. They hadn't had much to say. Of course they had messages from relatives and friends, and had done their best to comfort her, but they had seemed withdrawn, uncomfortable.

She wasn't really surprised. After all, it might have been the second to last time they ever saw her alive. She quickly tried to suppress that thought. There didn't seem to be any point dwelling on it: she couldn't do anything about it anyway.

It was going to be awkward when her parents came: she could foresee that. She wasn't sure what to do. Should she say goodbye to her parents in case she did not pull through – but how would she possibly go about that? Would they try to do the same to her? If she did, and she did come through, it would be embarrassing, as if she had felt defeated before the battle began, and hadn't expected to survive. And yet, if she did not, and she didn't pull through, she would have left them without telling them how much she loved them, how much they meant to her.

The nurse had come in again. This time she caught Joanna with her eyes open, and began wittering on in the inane fashion that nurses invariably do when attempting to entertain a bored or nervous patient.

Joanna listened patiently, trying to laugh, smile, nod her

head and look sympathetic at regular intervals, but her mind was elsewhere. She wished the woman would just leave her alone.

She wondered groggily what was going on.

She must have fallen asleep. Her parents seemed to have materialised out of nowhere, and were looking at her anxiously, yet with fixed smiles on their faces. It was a strange, if somewhat alarming sight. She could see a large trolley of ominous-looking instruments, and a portable bed, both of which had not been in the room earlier. She glanced at the clock, and her heart sank as it told her what she did not want to know.

So this was it. She was about to be voluntarily put into a sleep from which she might never awake. And even if she did . . .

They gave her a pink, revolting looking liquid to drink. It's a pre-med, she was told. It will make you feel better. She looked up at their smiling, encouraging faces, all crowded around the bed, peering down at her, with distaste.

It was all so false, impersonal.

She drank the liquid obediently. It tasted fractionally worse than it looked. She was then manhandled on to the rickety metal portable bed and wheeled through a confusing maze of passages, halls and corridors. She was vaguely aware of her mother and father, hurrying alongside her, calling to her, holding her hand. She was becoming drowsy. She tried to fight it, but she couldn't. She wasn't sure what was happening.

They came to an abrupt halt.

Suddenly a green man came and stood over her. She noticed hazily that he had revolting breath, and a hideous smile.

He was telling her that she would be OK.

He produced a long needle. He tried to stick it in her. It hurt so much.

He kept doing it again and again, getting red in the face. Finally he seemed to succeed.

He was saying something. What was he saying? Count? Aloud? Up to five? Why? OK. Anything to stop him breathing on her.

'One.' The word came out somewhat indistinctly.

'Two.' Her voice was decidedly slurred.

'Three.' She was having trouble controlling her voice.

'Four.' A great numbness swept her entire body . . .

And everything went black . . .

Kate Davis (9)

Justin Fleming (14)

Esther Saxey (13)

SHAFTESBURY'S CHURCHES: AN ANTHOLOGY

Some poems to be taken with a pinch of imagination

ST PETER'S	*A Finding*
ST JAMES'S	*A Leaving*
ST RUMBOLD'S	*A Returning*
ST JOHN'S	*A Death*
THE ABBEY TREASURE	*A Legend of Life*

A Finding – St Peter's

Stranger
Look down on our world
Where the spiders shiver and the candles burn
   Where hundreds of catechisms
     Are buried in the pages
       Of thousands of books
Where the sacristans of centuries
  Waft the incense of memory . . .

      Where the walls are chill and holy.

Where the spiders shiver and the candles burn
Look down on our world
Stranger
And learn.

A Leaving – St James's

They say the world is round, and so
The road that takes me far,
Will also bring me back again
And closer to this door.

      I hope I may return again
      To smells of fresh-mown grass,
      And daisy-heads and battlements
      Where high-flung swallows pass

I hope to sense the awe again
The reverence to feel
Which when I was so young, bore down,
And made me humbly kneel

      If I may not the tower climb,
      The wind blown in my face,
      If I may not return again,
      I will not leave this place.

If I may not return again
And feel, midst heat of day
The cool which is to me St James's
I will not go away.

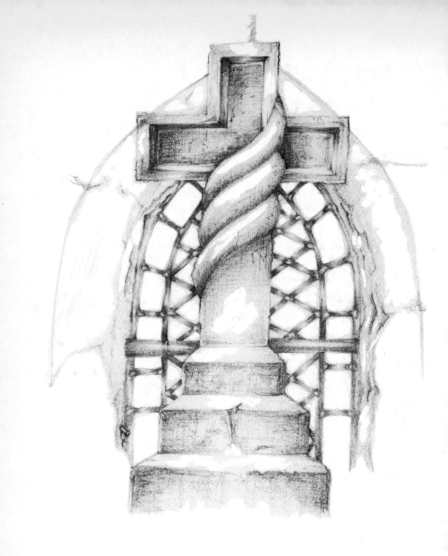

Nick Shearn (15)

A Returning – St Rumbold's

I will stand on the step
And open the door
And quietly pace
The high-polished floor

And no matter how softly
My feet touch the ground
The noise of my footsteps
Will echo around

And after a while
I'll find that whilst walking
The silence reduces
To whispers my talking

And I'll turn once again
and pace back to the door
Away from my face
In the high polished floor

For I am afraid
That now I have grown
The face in the floor
Is no longer my own

A Death – St John's

It may have been a body, once –
   An epitaph, a name:
A human being free of life
   Not to its spirit tame

            (Dust to dust, ashes to ashes)
            Rots in a tomb as a century passes.

(Cold letters carved on a dead man's memorial –)

All lives so long dead are just the same.
Not even a memory
Not even a tombstone
Not even an epitaph
Not even
a name

The Abbey Treasure

Come traveller, come pilgrim weak,
Come hunter chasing deer,
And search the ground
   'Till you have found
      Your hope is buried here

            I stood once in the Abbey proud
            I saw the bible taught
            Some magic ran
               From God to man
                  And with it I was wrought

Catherine Timson (9)

Then Henry's hand it smote the land
They hid me in the mire
They dug me deep
  In this dark sleep
    They quenched my golden fire

            A metre down, a century down
            And I have waited long
            They told me they'd
              Return some day
                The decades prove them wrong

But now my jewels lose brilliance here
My silverwork will rust
And nature's power
  Works hour by hour
    To turn my heart to dust

By Holy Spirit was I blessed
With ritual and with rhyme
I will not die
  In some way, I
    Will stand the test of time.

            Come traveller, come pilgrim weak,
            Come hunter chasing deer
              And search the town
                Five centuries down
            Your legends buried here.

Amy Taylor (8)

* THE SILK RIVER

Many spiders weave the river
Running through the green grass land.
It took them many years to weave,
But still they calmly go on weaving.

All the frogs and snakes come out
And say hello to all the spiders.
Then the frogs come out and sing
Their ancient songs to all of them.

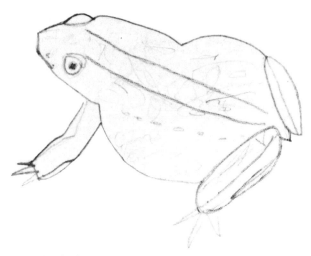

Victoria Luke (12)

Una Garvey (8)

* THE BAKERY

One morning, in spring, a little girl called Gwenda went to the bakery. Gwenda loved to snuggle down and enjoy a good bun. Gwenda nearly always went to the bakery to get a cake, scone, bun or bread. Her mother and father owned the beautiful bakery. They had taught Gwenda how to use the till, get the right cake, scone, bun or loaf of bread and give the right change and take the right money.

Today Gwenda was told to go and open the shop and work in it while they went to Auntie Rose's house for an hour. Gwenda loved working in her parents' shop. So she replied, 'I'll go in to work.' In went Gwenda. She heard her father's car drive off.

'I'm all on my own,' thought Gwenda, but she was wrong.

'Look at her,' whispered a voice. Gwenda heard it. 'What is she doing here?' another voice whispered. 'I . . . is . . . someone h . . . here?' stammered Gwenda. 'Do you know that we talk?' asked a currant bun. 'Why you're a bun,' said Gwenda astonished. 'Well of course I'm a bun. Make sure no one eats me,' said the currant bun. 'Guard us too,' called all the scones, buns, cakes and loaves of bread. 'But then I won't make any money and I will be scolded by my parents,' cried Gwenda. The leader of them all, the currant bun, was about to speak when someone came in.

'Good morning,' said Gwenda cheerfully. 'What can I do for you?'

'I'd like that currant bun for my wife.' It was a man who came in.

'No,' whispered the currant bun. 'Don't let him take me.'

Gwenda forgot that all the delicious food was real. 'That bun is fifty pence,' Gwenda said. Gwenda went to take the bun off the shop window. The currant bun ran like mad round the room. Gwenda then remembered that they were real. The man went pale and went out of the shop. Gwenda closed the bakery because she was also afraid.

Now she never volunteers to mind the bakery. Is it a dream or not? She wants to know that too!

Emma Devonald (5)

AT MIDNIGHT, IN MOONGLASSES

Thomas Dearsley (10)

Helena Echlin (14)

* **IN SOUTH AFRICA**

Just as the white might go sunbathing,
Letting light darken them,
Surely a black moonbathes?

At midnight, in moonglasses,
Thousands must sneak out,
And lie on the beaches,
In the light of the moon,

Trying to absorb that peculiar silver,
To become pale as milk,
Leaving no coke-cans or orange-peel,

For the white to stumble on,
Arriving at dawn,
Burning to darken.

Bikiron Banerjee (14)

* **KING OF THE AIRWAVES**

The metropolis is busy and bursting with life. I can see it with my headset. I sometimes control the tiny beams of light, sprawled across the city, carrying people to their destinations. One Zero is my name, night driving is my trade, although I also enjoy taking over at control. I am available for hire at moderate cost. Travellers all, do not hesitate to avail yourselves of my services. Put your trust in my competence. Sit back in the back, or up in the front. Place care to one side, your baggage on the other. One Zero is about to take you for a ride.

I am the Night Controller, satisfaction is my game. Call Angel Base from eight to eight, my voice will be there to welcome and convey your needs across the airwaves to the nearest mobile driver. You will not have to wait for long. I shall not publicise my virtues, but neither shall I suppress them. I am a dab hand on the wheel of my car, stupefying my unbeatable knowledge of the ins and outs of my part of London.

I take it as it comes, and them with it. They come and go so quick sometimes. I've only had time to push a stray wisp back into place, open myself up to the big wide world, and where I thought there was one, there's another. Good thing they've got numbers. It's funny at first, knowing them like that. It seems impersonal. It's better with the other system. No names. A number, a voice that's all. When the voice and the face changes you have still got a number to hold on to. You can say 'Come in Two Four, nice to have you on the air,' and you forget that last week's Two Four had a quiver in the middle range, and that a year ago it was a young boy with blue eyes and a disposition as liquorice on an empty belly. Yes, they come and go. All except One Zero, that is.

I place the headset upon my auburn curls and settle myself snugly against the cushions. I am ready. The phones ring, the radio bleeps, 'Yes, madam, we'll have a car with you, right away.'

Out there are the drivers, the night drivers and the people with a destination to meet, each needing the other. The drivers are lines of light in my mind, glow worms crawling over the grid of my territory. They are on the look out for commands, their endless trails, intersecting, converging, running parallel before shooting off at obtuse angles prompted by a difference of opinion as to how to get from Marble Arch to Pimlico on a Friday night in the late summer or perhaps a sudden instruction from the gloom of Angel Base.

My brain extends outwards over the grid, like water, running free into every crevice of a street, every hole of an impasse. The air is thick with information. I sort through it, censoring the unrepeatable and challenging the improbable. My fingers are institutions, splayed across whole borroughs, my hands reach into the interiors of cars, pluck, push, guide and give advice.

I am the King of the Airways and I have power. I sit on my black leather throne and put on my headset crown. I order my servants on wheels to fetch and carry, and they drive around in a frenzy until their mission is complete, only to be handed another in the space of a short minute.

The Prime Minister controls Britain, the Queen owns Britain. Richard Branson owns the world!

I control and am the heart of my kingdom, Catford.

** THE BOATMAN TREATMENT

The summer I was offered the job of attendant at the kids' ballpark behind the supermarket for six-fifty a half-day was when I began noticing how many ghosts I could see from my high-backed umpire's chair. Just around, like all the little kids, draped over the two-bit rides and the lottery ticket machine surrounded by dusty peanut shells, scuffling among the jacks and rubber balls, playing and watching. It wasn't the first time by any means; for months I had occasionally bumped into one – maybe in the elevator on my way up to the eleventh floor of Maria's apartment building, or hauling the groceries into the back seat of my mother's car, or just sitting looking at the ducks bobbing with their pursy little crests on the skinny lagoon in Mercourt Park. I'd feel a kind of buzzing in my belly, like a bee in a bottle, and I'd turn around, and there they'd be, just looking and waiting.

Of course, the first couple of times I looked away again, because it felt kind of terrible to be staring up at a greenish face with its perky little smile like a strawberry razorcut just blowing in and out in the middle. Then, when it became more regular and I got so's I'd feel cheated if I managed the walk to the cigarette stand without so much as a fleeting glimpse or a wave. I became bolder, and started sharing my peanuts, or popcorn, or figs, or whatsoever I kept in a greasy little bag in my camely pocket just in case I ran out of conversation.

My mother taught me that. When I was young, perhaps eight or nine, she sat me down with her freshly scalloped hair smelling of violet slick and spray, and she told me always to keep a little something – a package of cough-drops, or a wafer biscuit tucked into the pocket of my overalls just in case I struck up with a kind, hungry guy, or someone I had nothing to say to, and I could break the silence with a polite smile and press whatever the hell it was into his palm with a little flourish, knowing that I had manners.

In fact, it was raisins the day I first offered something, and I was flattered when a bony little hand clasped round them and kind of shoved them into a yawn that circled round for a minute and then slopped into a grin. I don't know why I hadn't noticed them so much before. It just seemed like there were so many, all over, knock-kneed on the buses and trains, and no one else batting so much as an eye. Maybe they all came at once, on a boat ride up the lagoon, and I was meeting them off their boat with smiles and dried fruit, as the sullen dogman in the ferry whaled back and forth for new passengers.

I immediately found myself wishing I had been taught, instead of geography maybe, how to make a conversation. All my life, I have been one of those people at parties who sits on the edges of people talking, and watches all the witty turtleneck men converse with the animated nylon women, and praying all the while that I would be able to do that someday. It's not that I don't have opinions. They're all muddled up when I'm with people, but when I'm on my own I'm so arrow-pure I could be the country's top diplomat. In fact, the only person I used to be able to talk to with any kind of conviction was myself. I'd have long, intense conversations with myself in front of the cracked ladies-room mirror in my father's store, before it was sold; about the new missiles, or Pearl Harbor, or who really killed Marilyn Monroe. I even managed to return busloads of faulty irons and fused plugs, inside the glassy privacy of that mirror, when in my real life I'd have shrugged sadly at the wasted money and kept the check for someone braver to wave indignantly under the superior noses that stood behind all the store counters. For the first time in my life I became busy. I'd sit at the ballpark, with one eye on the little kids, and the other watching my pencil scratching down records of all the new dead men that came to see me. By August I'd filled three folders. Some of them I only saw once, and they'd get back in their old canoe with the dogfaced man at the helm and that would be that. I'd never see them again. There were some, though, who came often. Old Joe, the guy who drowned in his bath while his wife and two kids were out bowling. He was tall, maybe five feet eleven, and he had these beautiful, withered little hands that he pushed back his hair with and tucked into my pockets for warmth. And Lula, the young black girl who killed herself for a lover. She was one of my favourites. She'd lived out west and worked on a farm, had fallen in love with this white guy named Ned who worked the ploughs and the farm machinery, and because she was black and he was white, she drowned herself in one of the big vats where they stored milk to make it into cheese.

I wrote page after page, all with dates and names and what they told me, and I felt that cosy pigeon-satisfaction that people get when they're sure of their friends; and when my mother asked me why I stayed out so late, and came home smelling of damp, I kept my mouth shut and went upstairs to read all my notes and wait for taps at the window.

I don't know to this day how the hell they managed to get to the balcony outside my bedroom, since we lived on the fourteenth floor, and there was a janitor, or an elevator man, or somebody, patrolling each storey until dawn. I just know that I grew to need to hear the familiar scratching on the pane, and I'd let whoever it was in, in a heady rush of warm air and old clothes, and they'd slink past me and slump down in my hard-backed chair, and I'd start talking. I made sure there was a jug of water, or some flowers, or something pretty that I could show my visitors

116

Lucy Sizer (16)

when they came, and they started coming every night. Sometimes just one, or maybe four all at once, and I'd find myself with the hostess dilemma of where everybody was going to sit. And when I got sick, they kind of made sure that there was someone with me all the time. Of course, they had to get out pretty quick when my mother came up to see me, or the doctor, and I'd lie there in a sweaty giggle, only half-listening; and watching the feet that nobody else saw wriggling behind the curtain.

When I got better and I was allowed back to school, I'd walk, with Eva usually, the little girl who was knocked down by a motorcycle, and she'd jump and jitterbug along the sidewalk like a puppy, holding my hands, or asking to be carried, or stopping for me to do up her shoelaces or fix her braids. And I was well and doing my lessons, and I slunk from one class to the next with my bag of books, and looked out of the window into the street.

They never came to school – none of them. They'd hesitate at the gate, and then run off, waving backwards, and it would be four o'clock at least before I opened my mouth again. I couldn't understand why there was so much fuss about dead bodies. Once there was an accident outside our block, on the corner of the street, and everybody was screaming. I stepped right to the front and looked, and looked at the man with the car mowed right over his belly, and his neck split, and his goggle eyes, and I watched him get up, holding on to his trousers, so he didn't spill, and disappear quite happy in the direction of the dogman and his ferry, while all the whitecoats scooped up old arms and legs and cabbagey heads and bundled them in a kind of awkward pile into the ambulance, driving away in a blue, honking mess.

Actually, I tell a lie. I used to be so afraid of bodies, and blood, before this summer. I guess it was because I was five when I saw my first dead person, and because it was my father, and I was the only one in the house. I was kind

118

of frightened and disappointed and squeamish all at the same time. In fact, it was a spring night, and so it was quite light outside, and the curtains were letting in this thin, bluish mist that rumbled into the bedrooms and draped over the house like so many rags. I'd woken up, because I'd had one of the dreams again, and I figured that my father must be pretty lonely too, what with my mother at the hospital and all, and I planned on getting into his bed and we'd have hot milk and go to sleep with settled bellies.

I sort of slunk around the door, which was hard because there was a chair against it. For as long as I can remember, whenever my mother was away, at the university, or at my grandmother's when she died, my father would stack a chair against his door in case somebody tried to get in – like a burglar or somebody. I stepped round the chair and ran over to his bed. I didn't even notice that the light was on, because if there was one thing my father was not afraid of it was the dark, and looking back it was pretty unusual to have that bright light beaming right on to his face while he was sleeping.

So I got right up on to the bed, with my nightdress all caught up in my legs, and when I saw his face and his eyes, and his body curled right over the pillow, I just stopped and looked. My father used to wear these sort of gowns in bed. They were a bit ragged, but he said they were cool and comfortable, and though I used to be a little embarrassed if one of my friends was sleeping over, with my dad in a dress and all, I thought they were beautiful too, with all the Mexican zig-zag stitches blazing green and red and yellow at the yoke. Anyhow, he was in one of these gowns, and he was lying almost horizontal, with a pillow stuffed against his belly and his feet poking stiff out the side of the covers, and I knew something was wrong. In the empty still of the early morning, I heard the dial tone buzzing. The telephone was off the hook, and smugly upright on the little desk on my dad's side of the bed. It was odd, too, because he was lying completely on the wrong side, over on my mother's side. He used to always sleep on the right, by the window, and my mother on the left, near the door. This time he was half-way down and very definitely in my mother's place. I thought he was sleeping so I tried shoving him a little to wake him up. My father had always been a very heavy sleeper. In the mornings, when I came in with the bread and the marmalade it took me three tries at the least to get him to open his eyes. The funny thing was, this time his eyes were very open, and I still couldn't rouse him. He was heavy, too, and cold, though it was a warm night; and when I noticed the little yellow puddle next to his mouth and the dirty, greenish blotches on his face, I just got off the bed and went to my room and when I woke up the next morning I went to school as if nothing had happened. It might not have done, too. After all, it's almost thirteen years now and I could just be making up the whole thing.

I was quite surprised my father never visited me, actually. I met so many, I just figured he might come along too, but he didn't. And one day, all of a sudden, they stopped. I left it about a week. I thought maybe there was something wrong with the boat, or they just wanted to stay home for a while – after all, it was always them who had to make the journey. I guess I would have done it, got into the boat and sailed off to wherever it went, but I figured maybe it was a private place, and I didn't have much money for the fare, and anyhow I was a little bit afraid of the man with the dog's head who never smiled.

But even after a week, still no one came. I stopped going to school. I stopped washing and sleeping and eating and I stayed in my bed with all my piles of notes and I read them, all my meetings over the summer months with Lula, and Old Joe, and Mrs Christiansen, and I read them all aloud, in my toneless voice, all through the day and night.

I figured if they heard me say their names often enough they'd come back, and everything would go on the same as it always had. My mother cried all the time, and so many different people came to see me, and I was driven through the mushroom-coloured autumn roads in my mother's car to countless different places; and I stayed the night in countless different hard beds, and was prodded and probed by different people all with one face, and I lost all my hope and let it happen.

Even when I had to sit in the little cubicle without my clothes, and with all the water, and when they wired me, and I shot like a terrific lightning scream right into the depths of my own throat and tongue, and when all those silver faces boomed down on me, still no one came. I lost all my notes. I saw them being locked away in a cabinet the colour of ash, and I was allowed nothing but the trays of stinking slush and the baths and the pans, and my tongue became thick and dry because I never spoke a word.

In fact I had given up all hope of ever getting back to my house, though I knew it wasn't far from where I was because I kind of recognised things when I sat by the window, before I was dragged away again to lie down on my bed.

And it was when I had completely given up on ever speaking again, or seeing any of them again, that I woke up one cold night and I opened my eyes, and the room with all its beds and frames and sleeping people was full of a grey-green sea full of all of them I had ever known, and some whom I had never known, and Old Joe came and took my hands and led me out of the bed and out of the window and out into the city with all its lights and darkness and the vague honking from the quayside. I was talking loudly and I felt the crusty bark that had been my tongue spring into life and I was singing, and we all ran like hell into the park, past the gates and the trees and the old benches, and I sang until I thought I would come right out of my own mouth and roll away into the lagoon.

The lagoon. I was standing there in my bare feet, and suddenly I was alone. I could hear the swishing of the night and a faint dripping, and all of them had disappeared, and I was holding my nightgown in bunches where the firm hands had been. And then the boat drew up, with the dogfaced man and his paddles, and I was the only passenger. And I stepped in, noticing how calm he was, and how gentle, and how beautiful his old gown was with all the Mexican stitching in red and green and yellow at the yoke; and we paddled noiselessly into a dark cove and I felt a sharp prick in my leg, and the water was green in my mouth, and tasted of dew and oldness and I was calm again.

And when we arrived at the shore, and the dogfaced man tethered the canoe to a chair that stood on the bank, I saw a white-coated woman wheeling someone that looked like me, or someone else I knew, and I saw my mother's face with all its tears, and I was filled with a kind of still happiness that almost broke my heart.

That was a long time ago. I never go back. I wouldn't leave this place for the world, and the only time I step past the shore is to wave to the ferryboat man as he whales back and forth with new passengers, and a smile on his dog's face.

Jamie Pike (10)

Steven Mercer (13)

THE BAT AT NIGHT

I

When the eagle
Tamed the wind,
And planted it
Within her feather-scarred – – – – –
Feather-mothered skin!

When the otter
Squeezed the river bed
Between her claws,
And carved it in the image
Of God –
The River Queen!

When the Owl
Clawed her eyes onto the wind,
And hooted a hoot
In the name
Of her night-time dream!

When this!
When this all blossomed
In flower and petal
Of night-sea wind!

Emma Idle (10)

The sun became
Melting cheese upon black-burning
Toast,
Melting and dripping,
River-playing around the plate,
And then falling –
Ocean-paddling on the floor.

The Sun
Became a cheese-grilled
Scar,
Rippled and wrinkled,
Ploughed sea-deep upon my palm.

And the moon
Became a silenced smudge
On my other palm

Cardboard-white upon concrete-black!
Shiver-white upon a ghostly sea-bed!

A half-digested splinter
Upon a heavily bearded horizon,
Tickling my throat.

II

I searched
For him,
And found him
Leather-domed upon my palm.

Watching me!
  Desiring me!
    Joining his wings
      With my hands!

I searched
For him,
And found him – – – – –
A sail upon the wind.

A sail of leather brooks
And empty streams –
He gave me his blood
And I gave him mine,
And we shared it like brothers –
Twins of the heart – – – – – –
Twins of the feather – – – – – –
Light of the sky!

Craig McCarthy (11)

III

I searched
For him,
And found him
Giving me his wings!

And found him
Giving me his wings
So that I might fly!
Break free
From the sight-prison
Of my eyes.

IV

And through my trust,
He gave me
His eyes,
So that I might see!
Breathe!
Feel!
The Pulses!

The Rock-pulses!
The River-blood
Of his
Wind-free wilderness.

And then flap!
Whip!
My leather trunks.
Upon the nostrils
Of a mighty wind.

So that
When I cry
The wind shall cry.

And when I die
The birds will mourn
And will no longer fly.

Harriet Earis (10)

BARN OWLS

Their hosts sing the sun away
And a fathom deep in dark they come
As ghosts in the gloaming.
The silent Solomons of light, and wise.
They do not dart with the swallows
But swoop in wrongside arches by the trees.
The stars are their only leaders to the moon.
For they are pinnacles of the night breeze
In close-wrapped dark.
In mystic presence they moonshine the globe
Till their feathers are submerged.

Euan Forbes (11)

Ben Abrahams (11)

* **SAVED**

I walked in.
A man with
Blood dripping
Down his
Shining nose
Is coming.

I see the anger
In his eyes.
His cheeks
are full of
The rose's thorns.
He's hit me.
I am bleeding.
I see
Death coming closer.
More thorns in me.
Flames
All around me.
People like the Devil
Drinking the wine
From my garden.
No, it can't be.

It's my brother
Sniffing the scent
Of the sweet roses.
My Mum's here.
Yes, saving me
From the lava pit.
She's killing them.
Yes, go on,
On, we've won,
Mum. Mum.

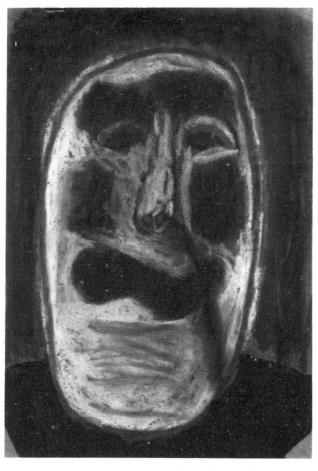

Rebecca Ryan (9)

Christopher Pattle (6)

* **DEATH IN THE TRAP**

Where's the castle with the
   mountain.
The sea round where the man
   died.
In a trap in a trap.
His remains are only his skin.
The people of the village took
   him to the pond.
Threw him in.
Covered the pond with silk.

LOSING THE COLD WAR

Simon Gordon-Lennox (12)

Marnie Smith-Hayes (12)

* **MASTITIS**

How she suffers,
A cow.

When her udder is hard,
As cold as winter's web,

She strikes her calf away,
As it tries to suck,
Strikes, not meaning to hurt!

She bellows!

The icicles form on her breath.

Her udder bursts,
Rotted,
White milk flows,

Rapids on water.

She falls,
Sleeping death,
The ice overtakes her,
And the cold wind tears her away.

Samantha Scriven (11)

Gary Downes (12)

Hannah Edwards (12)

* THE PHEASANT

The pheasant is the convict of the bracken world,
as he runs stumbling haphazardly.
A line of beaters stands ready to advance.
The signal is given
and the air rings
to men's bellowing voices
and sticks banging the bracken
that cracks under the frying sun!
The convict is sighted
and the only way is up,
up into the vast empty palette they call the sky.
He takes off like an unco-ordinated puppet,
but where is the get-away car?
As the pheasant heads over the trees,
The enemy works the puppet.
He looks down the silver-plated kaleidoscope eyes
at the double barrel gun
and in a feather ruffling
Screaming
eyes rolling second,
the pheasant falls like a clod of soil
earthed by a shot that drained the Electricity of life.
A last nerve flickers
and he dies.
Now he hangs by his neck in our garage.

William Mair (11)

SIAMESE FIGHTER

The Siamese Fighter suits his name,
A strong, boastful character
but a small fish in body . . .
A tiny petal floating about the tank.
His skin is the colour of an over-ripe plum,
Silky, smooth but tough with fighting.
He mopes around
attacking tiny fish out of pleasure.
Bored,
He needs excitement
in his confined glass world,
Like a small child on a Sunday morning.
He is king of the tank,
His fleshy fins of nylon
manoeuvre his model body around,
His eyes flash
like broken glass in the sun,
moving around,
staring,
looking you in the eye
but looking right through you,
blind.
His soft, metallic body
in . . .
oily canvas stretched over a plaster cast body,
but,
his life is not filled.
Empty he dies;
his glass eyes are dull as he floats to the top,
abdicating from the throne.

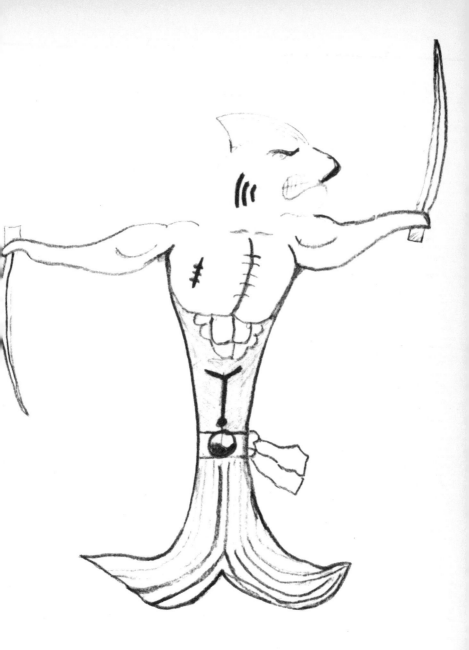

Joe Binder (13)

Nadav Drewe (8)

THE FROZEN FLOWER

A flower crystallised in glassy ice,
Purple petals unmoving in the cold embrace.
Frozen in time, the colours glisten in the brittle frost,
But as the beauty fades within the melting ice,
The flower wilts,
Sad that no seeds are carried on the wind
To ease its death and decay.

Simon Jarvis (10)

Emma Buckingham (12)

*   **THE WINTER SEASHORE**

Frost nipped at our ears and ankles,
Leaving them pinched pink.
We dodged tiny wet mirrors of water
And our mouths breathed eggs of steam.
Climbing the great bank of sandy shingle was
    impossible.
Each footstep of sand tumbled down
And took you with it.
Then, at the top of the giant barricade,
The almighty mouth of water
That had swallowed sand and cliffs
And if we were not careful, it would swallow us.
And now as I looked out to sea,
There was no skyline, just a vast palette of murky paint.
We walked, but the wind was so strong
That it blew us into a sidestep,
Then a lunge,
A sidestep, then a lunge,
A dislocated pattern.
This wind played games with our minds.
This sea,
Frosted in motion, took us in his hands,
And swallowed us.

Anna Rubins (14)

* **THE GIFT OF THE STORM**

I must have been eight or maybe nine at the time my parents died. Too young anyway for the reality to sink in. All I remember of my moving to Greyhills was a blur, something far removed from my childish world of marbles, scrapes and hide-and-seek. I remember only the huge black door-knocker, almost too heavy for me to lift, and my grandmother's pinched, sharp face staring down at me when she opened the door. I went to stay with her in Greyhills because she was the only family I had left, but she didn't seem like a family to me. Her sharp, abrupt voice was always ordering or criticising and her thin, pink lips were always pulled tight in annoyance.

It is strange that I cannot recall my parents' death because I can remember so many other things all too clearly, mostly loneliness. My old friends left behind in Sussex, I found it hard to make any more. Life had been so easy, I had lost the skill. The boys at my new school did not tease me exactly, but they did not like me either. I could tell that, so I was surprised that Tom allowed me to talk to him at all. Tom was the sort of boy my grand-mother, or even my parents, would have called 'a nasty piece of work'. But he and his friend Billy were human company and I was prepared to be their lap dog just so that terrible loneliness wouldn't return. I could always feel the mockery bubbling in them, just below the surface. Sometimes they would exchange a look, and then I knew that I, however unknowingly, had done something wrong. We used to wander round a lot, down by the estuary. That is Tom wandered and Billy followed him and I, always the last, followed Billy. The estuary had tides like the sea, and when the tide went out, it left an endless expanse of flat, evil-smelling mud, the colour of a pencil lead. Often there were things embedded in it, like nuts in a bar of chocolate I often thought; old boots, leaky buckets, pieces of driftwood and even dead fish. Tom used to pick these up and shove them in my face. It was a sort of bravery test: if I cringed, I lost, if not they put up with me for a bit longer. I never cringed.

Upland, there was a more rocky area that would have been a bank if the ground had been very little less flat. Here there stood an old hut and a collection of driftwood. I never found out who the collector was and certainly nobody wanted it for the pile had become a mound that held endless fascination for Tom and Billy. But to me it was a place of misery. For when Tom wanted a joke he would ask me to wait for him in the hut. I had to because he told me to. Then he and Billy would run off. I was never sure what I was supposed to do; go after them or 'wait for them to come back'. So I waited in there for a long time, to be certain they'd gone. Then I would creep out and go home to a spanking about my dirty clothes. Whether this earned their contempt or respect I didn't know, but it made me come to loathe the place. The disgusting fishy smell and the four rotting walls covered in green slime (moss or seaweed, I couldn't tell) had become my prison.

It was after a particularly hard day and a particularly hard spanking that the storm came. I could hear it from my tiny bedroom where I lay, turning this way and that, desperately trying to sleep. The rain beat relentlessly down all night, determined to wash the earth clear to its bare bones. The thunder played a fearsome symphony of destruction in the sky, and the wind, jealous of the ease and grace of the ships, picked them up and hurtled them against the rocks, dashing them to pieces. More driftwood. I can say without doubt that I did not once shut my eyes that night. What I did do was think. For the first time in my life I began to think for and about myself. I realised in a sudden flash of enlightenment that no one could control my thinking. Tom could manipulate me and my grandmother could order me about, but they couldn't stop me thinking anything I liked about them. Laughter rose in me, I felt crazy and wild and excited and angry all at the same time – just like the storm must have felt that night. I tried out my power. 'Tom is horrible,' I thought. 'I hate him.' It was incredible. '. . . And grandmother,' I added so as not to give one an advantage. As I watched, a faint grey sun hauled itself up over the horizon. Dawn. 'I'm like the sun too!' I thought. 'Just breaking my way out.' I was at one with the world. We understood each other, that sun and I.

'I'm going out,' I thought and I knew it was true. I was going out. I thought; but I didn't plan. I looked at the window. I climbed out. I dropped to the ground. It didn't hurt. It couldn't hurt. The whole thing seemed like a dream, but more real than my other life had ever been. It was still raining so I must have got wet but I couldn't feel it. Life was too good now to worry about water. My footsteps took me, guided by fate, instinct, or habit, down to the estuary. The air still stank of fish but it was somehow a fresher, cleaner smell than the day before. I breathed in deeply and almost forgot to breathe out again for there, amongst the rocks, mud and driftwood was something I never imagined seeing there. It was a piano. Battered, broken and devoid of legs – yes: but still a piano. My mind rushed back to old scenes, pictures from a past I hadn't recalled in a long, lonely time. They were happy family scenes. Me as a child sitting on a cushion clapping my hands, watching my mother's swift and nimble fingers glide across the piano keys. Christmas: carols being sung, the tree and the wonderful, beautiful music. My father's hearty, good-natured voice: 'You've a real talent for music, son, we'll have to give

145

you lessons soon.' 'Go on Martha, give us another one.' At the centre of it was always the piano.

The piano, the piano, the focal point of our household. No matter what we were doing we all found time to sit around the piano in the evenings. My mother was always the best, of course, she was a professional. 'Some day we'll measure up to her, eh, Johnny-me-boy?' my dad used to joke. And here it was. As my string of memories unwound to the end, the piano remained. Not the same one, naturally, but a piano. So this was what I had been longing for all the time. In the evenings in that dark, musty house I had known that something had been missing, but I never knew just what. But the storm had known. It had washed it up for me and drawn me out of bed on that particular day. It was a gift. The gift of the storm.

I ran down to touch it. It was wet and rotting but it had the same familiar curves. I walked all the way around, touching it. I finally drew up the courage to touch a key. Nothing. I might have expected it but I hadn't. I could have cried my despair aloud. But something told me to go on. I pressed the next key and, oh joy, a note. C. It was so comforting, like an old friend. I continued up the scale. Only about six notes worked but that was enough. I looked at the piano's innards. Like a surgeon I fished around inside pulling out a few old bits of wood. Most of it could be repaired. Then inspiration came. I could renovate the piano! I knew our old baby grand at home inside out. I could do it! I would.

Now that I had a mission, I found my longing for company had gone. I managed to avoid Tom and Billy. I couldn't think about school. My head was full of scales and strings and A flats and B sharps. Sometimes I used my newfound power of thought and thought something horrible about Tom, but not often. The world passed me by for the next few weeks and nobody could work it out. But

I was happy. Every day I went to visit the piano. I gave it a lick of 'borrowed' whitewash, tied up a few strings or just tinkered. I made a stool of sorts out of rocks and driftwood. But though I'd lost interest in Tom and Billy it turned out they were still interested in me.

One day I was walking to the estuary as usual when I turned round and saw Tom and Billy following me.

'Haven't seen a lot of you lately,' Tom remarked. 'Where are you going?'

Now Tom was actually standing over me I realised that once you let people control you, they do it for ever. I could ignore him, I could think bad things about him, but I couldn't stand up to Tom. Not like this. And he knew it.

'Well?' said Billy.

'Er . . um . . . the estuary.'

I could have told them anything, why did I have to tell them the truth?

From then on it was like a bad dream where you can't move or speak, just go along with what comes. So I was helpless as they led me into the junk yard part of the estuary. The gulls screeched as if to wake me up from my trance but it was no good. We came over the rise. They spotted the piano as I had known they would as soon as some demon forced out of my lips the name of my destination. The piano. My life. My only love. My secret. But I couldn't defend it now. All I could do was sit on the pile of wood where Tom pushed me and watch. Watch as the two boys ran for the piano. As Billy stepped back to a respectful distance. As Tom climbed on to the piano, as he lifted a huge rock above his head and got ready to smash!

The discordant note of the piano smashing was like the screaming of a million lost souls.

Andrew Holt (7)

THE HURL

The wind howled making little waves on the pond.
Trees groaned, it whipped the windows making the
  panes creak.

Sheets fly up in the air, grit flies in your eye,
Roof tiles fly up as if they were paper aeroplanes.
The flying bug gets overpowered.

It blows, it howls, it whistles down chimney pots,
It hates things that are still.
If it cannot move them it tries somewhere else.
It whacks it, it whips it, it will do anything to make it
  move.

The wind hurls round leaves on the path,
Making gravel roll about.
It whacks bricks on the wall blowing bricks out of place.

Stephen Gardam (14)

** DUNWICH

On the corner, there is a walnut tree.
Stretching its gnarled limbs
High,
For the wind to turn its leaves
To face the sea.
To face the sea that didn't used to be;
When the walnut tree had no reason to stretch before
   the wind.

Now a car park, one or two tufts of rope blowing,
Commands the bottom of the picture;
A picture unframed; wild but tamed.
The new café to the right,
Marshy dunes to the left.
But, at the top,
The sea, the sky,
The fishing boats.
Carved, wood splintering,
Lying like a herd of well-fed
But hollow sea-cows
Then the sea.

Grey, tops of the waves just brushed with white,
With the farthest curve of the stony beach
Stuck niggling in one corner
With the crumbling cliffs
A line of formless village elders;
Elders of the village of Britain
Sat in a never-ending war council against the sea.

And losing the cold war.

Katherine Hawker (15)

THE OLD MAN OF CONISTON

'Tell me a story,' demanded the Boy.

'What sort of story?' asked the Grandfather, puffing at his pipe.

'A long one,' came the firm reply.

The Grandfather chuckled. 'What shall it be about?' he asked again.

The Boy thought hard, screwing up his face in the effort. 'About giants and dragons, and witches . . . and mountains,' he said at last.

'I shall do my best,' said the Grandfather.

There was a long pause. Outside, the wind whistled wildly around the little cottage, but inside was peace. The big clock in the corner, which was even bigger than the Grandfather, ticked away. The fire burned cheerfully on the hearth, shedding its cosy glow over the pair; the Boy with his face uplifted expectantly towards the Grandfather; the Grandfather himself gazing beyond the house wall at something unseen. Then he began.

'This is a story which my grandfather told me, and before that, his grandfather told him, and it was my grandfather's grandfather's grandfather who heard it from the Old Man himself. For this is the story of the Old Man of Coniston, who has slept now for years beyond count. My grandfather's grandfather's grandfather was the last Man to speak to him.' The Grandfather fell silent again.

'Did the Old Man live in the mountains, then?' asked the Boy tentatively.

'Oh dear me, no! He was . . . he still *is* the mountain itself . . . but I'm starting in the middle.

'The Old Man is one of hundreds of stone giants;

"Tains", who came out of the Sea directly after the Ice Age, when the whole world was frozen over. They would stride out of the Sea, walk a little way inland in the valleys, find a nice piece of high ground and sit down with their feet in the valley and their heads in the clouds. There were no Men around at that time in History, but there were plenty of witches and dragons. It has been said that the Tains were sent to banish or kill these before Men came.

'The Old Man was the very first of the Tains to come out of the Sea. He was old then; older than any of the other Tains – so old that no one could remember his real name, and he had been thinking about Land for a very long time. He would dream about it too, seeing great rivers and lakes and forests, but no Tains. He longed to be the first Tain to come to rest, with his feet in a green valley and his head in the clouds. And so he was the first. But it took a long time for him to find the resting place he imagined.

'Besides the lakes, rivers and forests, there were, of course, a great many dragons and witches in the North. Many, many fights he fought as he worked his way northward along a long river valley: the valley of the Crake river. At last a small band of the remaining witches and dragons fled over the high ground at the head of the valley. The Old Man heaved a sigh of relief and, looking around him, saw that this was the land of his dreams. So he settled himself on a nice piece of high ground, with his head in the clouds and his feet in the valley.

'Many months of days, and years of months the Old Man rested there whilst the grass grew upon his clothes and his hair and beard grew long and grey. Long time it seemed to him – and yet not long, as the sheep and goats trustingly grazed in his lap, and he watched and waited for the coming of the other Tains out of the Sea.

'First to come was the Great Grize who, in his pride, had thought that he was the first Tain on Land. When he saw the Old Man sitting in content, as he had been doing for many years, he was furious, but as he leapt forward to grab the Old Man, he tripped and fell down dead. The Old Man was so grieved at this that he wept great tears, which flooded the valley between the two Tains. Then the Old Man buried the Great Grize beneath a long pile of rocks and named the grave of Grize Grizedale. When this was done, the Old Man prayed to the Maker, the All-Father:

'"Father of All, I pray that the Fall of Grize may be remembered by all that lives, and may it be a warning that pride shall come before a fall. And in your mercy, Father, remember Grize as he was when You made him. May his grave be blessed, and all Grizedale be covered with trees."

'So, the Old Man's prayer was heard and granted and Grize, whose first vision of the Land was of great forests, himself supported the first great forest of the North.

'Soon the other Tains came out of the Sea. Scaw the Fell (brother of the Great Grize) and his sons Lang and Bow the Fell came first, and after them Skiddaw the Far-seeing, Helvellyn, Blencathra, Glaramara and others whose names have been forgotten and were re-named by the Men when they came. There were also many others who came out of the Sea further North or South, or who came out of the Eastern Sea.

'Of course Scaw wished very much to know where his brother Grize was, so he asked the Old Man if he had seen him. The Old Man told the sad tale. But Scaw did not believe him and shouted to his sons:

'"See! The lying Old Man has killed my brother, and now he hopes to deceive us. Let us teach him what it means to murder the Great Grize!" And he drew back his hand to smite the Old Man.

'But Skiddaw the Far-seeing stayed him, saying:

'"Wait! Do not strike the Old Man. Do you not know, brother of Grize, that no one can kill a Tain; no one but He who declares the life-span of all things, He who made us and all the Universe? For surely it is as the Old Man says. Grize was struck down in his pride by the All-Father. But do not be angry with Him. He is as merciful as He is just. Behold Grizedale, the grave of Grize your brother. In his mercy, the All-Father has honoured Grize and fulfilled his dream of forests. Also, in the fall of Grize, He has left us and all living things a warning. Ever after shall it be remembered that "Pride comes before a fall". Let you, proud Scaw, take that to your heart and allow the Old Man to forgive you for your hasty anger."

'Scaw repented of his proud words and the Old Man forgave him, and peace was restored among the Tains. Most now travelled northward to find their resting places. Scaw-fell may still be seen majestically towering over Wast Water; the two heads of Lang over the Lang-dale Valley and Helvellyn over the Thirl Valley, which was flooded to become Thirlmere. Skiddaw and Blencathra travelled far to the north of this country.

'And so, the Tains waited expectantly for the next great event in History – the coming of Men. For a long time there were rumours of Men in the South-East, where Tains were scarce, but at last Tains in the East sent messages to Skiddaw the Far-seeing:

'"Men are coming out of the great forests of the south. They seek new lands. They are coming at last!"

'At long last Men came, both over the Sea, and over Land; slowly at first, but more and more until the Land was filled with little settlements. The Tains welcomed them and the Men named the Mount-tains, because they had to climb high to speak with them. But they were distrustful of some. Scaw-fell they did not like, proud and tall and forbidding as he seemed. This was a punishment for his pride in dealing with the Old Man.

'A small band of Men under a man named Conise came up the Crake; the same river up which the Old Man had come so long ago. They settled at the Old Man's feet, calling the settlement Coniston in honour of Conise, and the lake of tears shed by the Old Man for Grize, the Water of Coniston, or Coniston's Water. Conise also went up to speak with the Old Man, and from him learned many things; legends and lore. Among these, he learned of the Fall of Grize and the Love of the All-Father. Then Conise named the Old Man, the Old Man of Coniston, for he sits over the village of Coniston protectively and was always their friend and ally in good deeds.

'When the Tains (or Mountains as they are called) came out of the Sea and destroyed the witches and dragons, not all were destroyed. Some fled northward, and some East and South, swearing to take their revenge on the Mountains. Only one dragon and three witches from the North-West survived, however. These all happened to be from the small band who had fled before the Old Man as he walked up the Crake Valley.

'Just after the time of coming of Men, Blencathra and Helvellyn sent a message to the Old Man, saying:

'"Three witches are coming down from the North; their names are Beller, Lever and Lower. They carry three great cauldrons and mutter of Tains and Mountains, and the Old Man and revenge. They kill many Men as they come. Despite all that we can do, they are coming steadily southward, and it seems it is you they seek."

'And the Old Man replied:

'"Let them come. This is one of the tasks for which I have been prepared, and I am ready for it."

'In the first light of dawn, the three witches went up to speak with the Old Man, bringing with them their cauldrons. It was a cold, cloudy morning; white frost was on the grass, and the grey clouds seemed unwilling to let light through. Beller, as eldest of the three witches, spoke to the Old Man:

'"Old Man, we are the three witches of the Crake Valley, Beller, Lever and Lower, whom you drove out in your arrogance as you rose out of the Sea. We are come to take our revenge."

'And the Old Man answered:

'"Revenge? Who speaks of revenge? Do you not know that the All-Father does not condone revenge? Have you not come to repent of your wickedness and folly? No. I see that you have not. Then you must prepare to face the consequences."

'This put Beller in such a rage that she danced up and down on the spot. When at last she could speak, she shrieked:

'"You old fool! Can't you see when you're beaten? You talk of an All-Father. Where is he? Everywhere and nowhere!" she spat. "Well hear me, Old Fool. You shall face the consequences of turning us out and stealing from us these contemptuous Men. We are come to take revenge. You like to sit on a stone and stone we shall make you!"

'All three witches poured the contents of their cauldrons out on to the Old Man. There was a long silence. Then, from deep within the Tain, there began a rumbling. It spread until the very ground trembled and the surface of the lake broke into hundreds of waves. At that moment, the sun broke out between clouds with amazing suddenness and brilliance. The witches fell down in fear and covered their eyes in an attempt to shut out the light and noise. The noise broke out like a great clap of thunder. The Old Man was laughing. He laughed long, causing even Skiddaw, far up northwards, to wonder what amused him. At last he stopped.

'"Witches of the Crake Vale," he cried, "hear me now, you fools. Did you think that you could turn a Tain to stone? We are the Stone Giants who came out of the Sea, the guardians of Men. None but the Maker, who decrees the life-span of all things can destroy a Tain. So hear now His judgement, you who scorn the All-Father. You who sought to destroy a Tain by stone, shall yourselves be destroyed by stone."

'At this, the Old Man stood up, sending the three witches tumbling down to the ground above the lake, next to the village of Coniston. On top of them fell a great many stones and boulders, which completely covered them (in later days, this great mound was covered with grass and bracken, and was known by Men as "The Bell"). The Old Man then sat down again and, taking the three great cauldrons, set one in the crook of his left arm (this, being Lever's, became known as Lever's Water); another in his left shoulder (this became known as Low Water) and the third he set in the crook of his right arm (although this was Beller's cauldron, Men now call it Goat's Water). These were filled with rainwater, which overflowed and ran in streams into the lake, providing water for the village.

'When these things were done and the Men back in the village, the Old Man rested for many years, speaking only to the shepherds and goatherds who drove their flocks on to the Mountainside.

'A hundred or more summers passed, when one winter's night the last remaining dragon of the North, Tilber the Terrible, suddenly flew in from the South. He was one of the dragons who the Old Man had driven out with the three witches, Beller, Lever and Lower. Tilber flew up the river in a burst of red-gold flame, making the water hiss and boil as he approached, and evaporate into little curls of steam. He was extremely surprised to see the lake filling the valley; he had counted on being able to land there and rest from his journey. He was also surprised to see the great hump of Grizedale on one side and the Old Man on the other. Since he couldn't land in the valley because of the lake, or on Grizedale because of the great forest which it supported, he flew upwards, singeing the trees as he went, and circled around the head of the Old

Man. When he saw that it was the Tain, he reeled backwards in surprise, but soon approached, snorting flames which scorched and frizzled the grass on the Old Man's head. Then he spoke:

'"So you are still here, then, Old Man. I should have thought that you would have wearied of these Men long before now, and gone back to the Sea where you belong."

'"You surprise me," rejoined the Old Man. "I should have thought that you knew Tains better than that. What is it that you want?"

'"Oh, I came to see the old place. It has changed greatly, what with you, and the Men, and that great lump the other side of the valley; and the lake, too . . . I had also heard that witches had come this way . . ."

'"Then take warning, Tilber. The hill by my feet is the grave of the witches Beller, Lever and Lower, who were struck down in their wickedness by the All-Father. Beware, lest the same happen to you."

'"You dare threaten me? Tilber the Terrible?" Tilber was enraged and looked for a place from which to attack. He settled on some high ground to the Old Man's left hand and began to burn everything in his path as he strove to reach the Tain. Then the Old Man took the great cauldron of Lever, which was filled with rain water, and poured it into Tilber's open mouth.

'All at once there was a gigantic bang and flames shot into the air. Taking Lower's cauldron, the Old Man poured it over Tilber's body, quenching the flames. The water ran down his sides in rivulets, forming the Greenburn Beck, and a great steam rose, curling itself around the mountain, only to be blown away by a fresh breeze which rose in the West.

'And so the fire of Tilber was quenched – and this, of course, is the best way to kill a dragon. Then, as with Grize and the witches, the Old Man shook great stones down from his sides and buried the great carcass. Ever after, that tumbling, brownland was known as Tilber-thwaite fells, and the peak at the dragon's head was called Wetherlam.

'After all his labours, the Old Man slept for many, many years – so long in fact, that the Men of the village could only remember a vague tale of dragons and witches and had almost completely forgotten about the existence of Tains. Then someone found copper in the side of the mountain and Men began to dig for it. This made the Old Man wake up. He felt very old and tired, especially now that Men were taking bits out of his side, but he didn't have the strength or the will to stop them. So he looked out across the valley day after day, remembering all his past days and years in this place. It was this time that he met a young shepherd who drove his sheep up the mountain in summer. To him the Old Man told this legend, and many others besides, many of which have been forgotten by all other Men. As the Old Man finished his tale, he sighed.

'"And now Men are taking copper out of my side. It is almost as much as I can bear."

'"Should I try to get them to stop?" asked the shepherd.

'"No. They will stop soon. It does not go deep. Then I shall sleep again."

'"How long for this time, Old Man?"

'"Oh, long, long time. Longer than you can comprehend. Yet it shall also seem short. I have to gather strength for the Last Rising of the Tains."

'"When will that be?"

'"Before the End of Time; before the Great Judgement. It is then that all the witches and dragons of the North who were banished, shall rise against the Tains and against Man. For that time I shall store my strength."

'At the end of a few years, the Men of the village could find no more copper, so they gave up and went home, or else dug for slate in the Tilberthwaite fells. Then the Old Tain slept again, but there shall come a day, towards the

End of Time, when all the Tains shall wake and help Men to fight against witches and dragons, and all the dark forces of the North.

'The shepherd was sad to lose his friend, but passed on the stories and legends to his grandson. That grandson, when he had a grandson of his own, told the same story. He, in turn, told it to his own grandson, just as I have told it to you.'

The Grandfather fell silent once more and neither Boy nor Grandfather stirred for a long minute, while the clock ticked on, the embers of the fire glowed and the wind tore around the corner of the cottage through the trees by the gate.

The clock whirred, preparing to strike. The Grandfather broke the silence.

'Come on, bedtime. All dragon slayers must sleep well.'

'Grandfather, is it true? Did all that really happen?'

'Do you believe that it's true?'

'Yes . . .'

'Then that is all that matters.'

NOTE: This legend is original and not based on any known legend of the Old Man of Coniston. All places mentioned are, however, completely real.

BARBED-WIRE SMILES AND
BARBED-WIRE KISSES

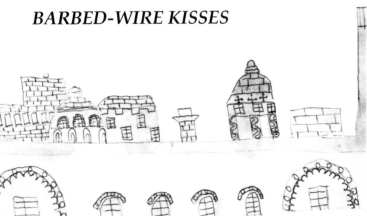

Helen Felcey (10)

Richard Colvert (16)

MANBIRD

'I can fly!' said the man in great secrecy.
'He can fly,' his friend told to others,
'A man with wings and who's able to fly.'
'He flies?' asked the reporter, voice tinged with doubt.
'A mutated man who is able to fly?'
The rumour spread from gossip to fact.
People questioned themselves – was it man or bird?
'He's a mutant,' said men in the streets later on.
'A mutant, a bird, a thing able to fly.'
'It can fly? Is it free?' asked the head of the state.
'Is it slain?' said the same man speaking with dread.
His agent replied with a nod of his heads.

Avril Huston (14)

** THE CORRESPONDENT

The nights were most terrifying of all.

She would lie there in bed, mummified by her fear of what lay outside the front door. Every time a footfall rang out she imagined him. The Attacker. He was a dim, shadowy figure of evil, and he was coming to get her. He preyed on her mind. When the stairwell outside echoed with screams, his face came, uninvited, into her thoughts, and he wouldn't go away.

On her front door there was a mortise lock, a peep-hole and a door-chain. Over these was bolted a thick steel grille. The windows were double-glazed and locked, and the flat was on the fourth floor.

'If I stay in here,' she thought, 'he won't be able to get me.'

The Attacker was a personification of the sick society which lay beyond her door. He was the rapist, the burglar, the murderer, the con-man, the 'ghost'. He was pure evil; she was terrified of him and everything he stood for.

And so, she stayed in the flat. Newspapers, groceries and clothing were delivered to her door. Even work came through her letter-box, as she had become a freelance writer after a man in the office had started to harass her. It was his face she saw beneath the Attacker's mask in her nightmares. It was him she was hiding from.

She kept her curtains drawn most of the time. It made her shudder to see the pale blue, watery sky draped, like a pair of faded jeans, over the tower blocks. And she believed that the Attacker was watching her, from the windows of the flat across the street, and gloating. He was just biding his time, waiting for an opportunity to . . . She shuddered again, and tugged the curtains closed.

One morning, she was reading the paper as usual, looking at the property prices and wishing desperately that she could afford to move, and possibly shake off the Attacker. Then a small advertisement with a box around it caught her eye. It was in the bottom right-hand corner of the page. It simply said:

Need a friend?
So do I
Write to –

and gave a box number. Suddenly, she realised how lonely she had been since her parents died. She tried to remember when she had last actually talked to someone. She spoke – on the telephone, and to the paper-boy and the people who delivered things – but never talked. It was the Attacker's fault. He kept her in her home, a fugitive from his threat. A lonely fugitive.

She went to the drawer where she kept her writing paper and stamps. Carefully, she selected an italic-nibbed pen and a bottle of pale blue ink. A sheet of creamy, thick, quality paper was slid gently from its packaging, and then another, and then another, as she articulated her thoughts and emotions on to them. Even though her feelings were as jerky as marionettes, they still marched across the pages of neat script, absorbing life from the pale ink.

Finally, an envelope was flicked open, and the neatly folded letter slid inside. The pen slipped silently across the sealed envelope, writing the address in impeccable italics. She detached a stamp from the sheet in the drawer and moistened it, the pink, delicate point of her tongue showing like a cat's. All that remained was a trip to the post office – out in the street. She stiffened with terror. She couldn't go out. It was too dangerous. She would ask the postman next morning if he would drop it in at the depot.

The postman arrived, his boots clattering along the

Sophie Rickard (10)

concrete hallway. She looked out of the peep-hole. He was only young, with fine, curly fair hair. He looked innocent. She opened the door slowly. Haltingly, she asked if he would mind posting it for her. She was relieved when he didn't ask why she couldn't post it herself. As soon as he had taken the letter, she thanked him and shut the door.

The mortise lock snapped shut, the cover slid back over the peep-hole, the chain rattled back into its hole. The steel gate, with its comfortingly chunky bars, swung over the entire ensemble and clanged shut. The bolts were rammed into place.

Outside, the postman listened to these operations, wondering why she was so unwilling to leave her home – and why she had bolted herself into it. He walked down the corridor to finish his deliveries, deciding to be friendlier to her in future. She seemed to be nervous. Maybe he could help. Her face remained in his brain, finely detailed, as infatuation slowly took its hold upon him.

A reply to the letter came, warm and understanding her feelings fully. She started to fall in love with the nameless correspondent. Romances waltzed through her brain, and she wrote to him every day.

The postman waited every morning, listening to the rattle of the locks and bolts and chains, ready to receive the letter. He smiled at her, talked to her, took the letter, wishing he had the courage to take her hand. She thanked him perfunctorily and slammed the door.

As she turned the key in the lock one morning, a thought struck her. Maybe the postman had been reading the letters. That was why he was all smiles. He probably thought it a great joke. Anger rose in her mind. That was it. No one was reading her letters to the Correspondent. Danger or no, she would go down to the post office herself. The letters were her secret.

In her mind at night, the Attacker still lurked. But now, the Correspondent stalked him, bringing him down. At last, night faded from her dreams, and they were all of her and the Correspondent, the Attacker gone for good.

On her daily visit to the post office, she picked up her groceries, rather than waiting for the delivery. She had joined the local library and the Residents' Association, through which she had made friends. Now, when the postman called, she was out, busy talking to the news-agent or changing books at the library or meeting a friend.

She had started her life again, with the support and encouragement of the Correspondent.

The postman, disillusioned, had quit his job and gone back to his home in Newcastle. His mum had been right about Southerners . . .

She checked herself in the mirror. Hair tidy, foundation even, eye-shadow neatly applied, lipstick well-defined, shoes polished, flowers carefully wrapped. She was ready to meet the Correspondent. What was she going to say – apart from 'I love you?'

As she walked along the road, she smiled at everyone she passed. People turned to smile back and to admire her neat figure springing down the street, towards the restau-rant where she would finally meet him.

The waiter escorted her to the table where the Correspondent waited. As she sat down, she noticed that he proffered flowers identical to hers. A bunch of six red roses . . .

The next detail she took in was his face. A face she had seen many times in dreams, beneath a mask – her hero and the focus of her fear and hatred had fused into one face. The Attacker was the Correspondent. Gasping with shock and pure terror, she struggled desperately to her feet.

He, too, was shocked. 'Janet,' he stammered. 'I'm sorry, Janet. I had no idea it was you.'

She laughed bitterly as the irony of the situation struck her. Her Messiah, the man who had pulled her out of her dingy little flat was also he who had forced her into leading the life of a recluse, he who had made her buy the steel grille, he who had made her afraid to sleep or go out. Her Christ and Antichrist were one.

And she had bought him roses.

Nicola Thompson (10)

Matilda Mitchell (16)

* **ALTER EGO**

That superficial arrogance you wear,
The confidence with which you flick your hair
Hides nothing, covers only wretchedness
At complications shading happiness.
You glance around – will someone see your flaws?
Your nervousness protrudes – not without cause.
Your insecurity is now revealed;
Your envelope of pride is now unsealed.
For someone, somewhere has the power to see –
That someone, somewhere happens to be me.

I notice, now, your spirit in disguise,
The vulnerability stored behind those eyes,
Detect a malice deep within your smile.
I comprehend an evil motive while
You contradict what others have to say;
They threaten your intelligence some way.
But have you noticed that I am not blind?
That I'm the one who's seen inside your mind?
Don't worry. For I will not turn your key –
I love you for the way you seem to be.

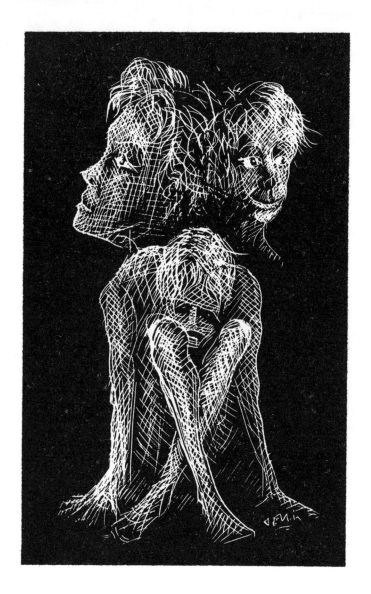

Tom Ellis (17)

Lydia Wharf (12)

SMOKER

I walked down the High Street,
And there was that bloke,
He stood on the corner,
Having a smoke.

It went in his mouth,
Past his yellowy teeth.
I could almost see,
Black lungs underneath.

But then – to my horror,
He blew it straight out,
Into my face –
That dirty great lout!

My fury, my anger,
They took hold of me.
It was quite disgusting,
I think you'll agree.

I turned straight around
And said to his face,
'You dog-breath! You chimney!
You human disgrace!

You're giving me cancer,
You and your fag,
I'm not a smoker,
I don't want a drag.

You think you're so trendy,
That thing in your trap,
First it's just one and then
Wow! The whole pack.'

Smoker

'You're wrong, I'm addicted,
I simply can't stop!
I try to give up,
But I feel like I'll drop.

At first it was cool,
I was one of the crowd,
Any non-smoker
Just wasn't allowed.

I know that I smell,
And I know it looks sick,
But this is a habit
I simply can't kick!'

Me

'You shouldn't have tried it,
You whopping great fool!
Ignore all the pushers,
The ones at your school.

Think of the tar,
That massive great load,
It could have been used
To cover the road.

And all over the world
Smokers are sighing
Because they know
Inside they're dying.'

Charlotte Wright (10)

CARLOS IN BUSSANA VECHIA

We have a house in Bussana,
Made of stone,
Old, the colour of sand.
Ten rooms, two balconies and a cellar
Make up our huge house.
One holiday
My friend Sophie came to stay,
One hot summer for two whole weeks,
Next door to us with her family.
Opposite lives Carlos,
In his twenties,
Chubby, with long curly yellow hair.
His face is a greasy pineapple,
His eyes are round and soggy.
He's always offering things in a mean way,
Is generous, in a mean way,
Hanging around us.
One day greasy Carlos said to Sophie,
'My dear blonde girlfriend,
Come, I'll buy you an icecream.'
But Sophie walked upstairs
With her previous icecream
Saying,
'Here,
Stuff this up your arse!'

Stephen Routledge (14)

HOMECOMING

Everyone has cause
to line the brick-a-brack road –
the little people.
Barbed-wire smiles,
and barbed-wire kisses.

The heavy rubber boots
bring up the dust
to mist the tears.
Hats that hide the scars,
men without limbs,
and death that juggles
with the mind.
This is how the war is won
or lost.

The poppies bleed our love for you
but they have stopped growing now.

I see your face –
the mask that's formed upon the past.
A slab of gravestone heart;
friends' names on a slate.
Your eyes
pits for the dancing devil
your tongue speaks
only on command.
And the time has come
when I can call you father again.

Trudy Allen (12)

THE TEACHERS AND THE CHILDREN

The teachers and the children
Went on a sponsored walk
The teachers led the children
And wouldn't let them talk
Up and down the hillside
Along the sandy beach
The teachers taking great big strides
I wish they'd only teach.

Sophie Dickerson (8)

Clare Broderick (6)

SO ANGRY

When I come home from school my sister plays in my room so that I say clean my room up. But she runs away. Then I have bad temper. I jump on my bed and I slap her but I wish I had not hit her now. I sneak in her room and mess her room up and I feel inside like a piece of wood burning in my tummy. Sometimes I kick things. If I had a magic finger I could turn Carly into a frog.

Helen Sparrow (5)

Sinead Wilson (15)

*   **HER VIEW**

The fire burns my edges
    turning them to crispy golden.
    No one noticed.
I could open my fist
        and see
           in the crevice of my palm
    a smouldering thing.
   What makes it burn so deeply?
   Thawing away my modesty
    Twisting and stretching
       up inside me,
the flame melting my body
       into tar.
You started it
   with the vodka you filled me
   and lit it
     with your smile.
I know you didn't mean to.
It was an accident
  I'm sure
    no one noticed
      except for me.

Helena Echlin (14)

* **TULIP**

A man turns to look as a
Tulip's red and yellow petals
Move slightly in the wind.

She pulls her yellow silks
Tightly across her body.
They outline her expertly.

When she sees a man pass
She ripples all over.
Her lipstick is as red as

Traffic lights saying stop.
It needs to be the kind
That doesn't smudge.

Saranaz Alizadeh (7)

She never has to
Give an invitation.
Her body does it all for her.

She's beautiful all over,
And she walks like she's got
Secrets between her thighs.

But her eyes keep out the light.
She just doesn't care.
It's like making love to a dead woman.

Except that it is not love.
Although it is her trade
She has never known love.

A man turns to look as a
Tulip's red and yellow petals
Move slightly in the wind.

JUST LIKE MY THOUGHTS LOOKING

FOR SOMEWHERE TO REST . . .

Christopher Bertrand (12)

Keith Malin (11)

THE IMPOSSIBLE ROBBERY

This robber was fed up with money,
And guns,
And cops,
And getaway cars.

This robber wanted to steal something different,
Like the heat of the sun,
Or the space between stars,
Or even the salt in the sea.

This robber wanted to steal something useful,
Like the wisdom of Einstein,
Or a fruit orchard,
Or even London Zoo.

This robber wanted to steal something rare,
Like a dinosaur's egg,
Or a coin from Atlantis,
Or even the taste of success.

Avril Huston (14)

** TURMOIL

I walk down the street:
My love for you is as a balloon
Expanding in my chest
And my ribs crack with the
Painful joy of it all.
There's a lot of passion flowing around
In here, you know:
A whole battery of emotions in
Disciplined riot, electrifying my skin,
Yet no mode of expression possible,
Because I can't let you know how
My feelings ripple in their vicious
Ring: love in a closed circuit.

Susie White (16)

James Mitchell (9)

A POETRY LESSON

It was half past two, Monday afternoon.
Just been called in from playtime.
Inside the dark class room
Hot and heavy with the summer's sun . . .

'Write a poem,
Write a poem about a butterfly.'

But where's the butterfly?
I can't write about a butterfly.
Unless I have one on my table.
Then I could watch its wings breathe,
And see its splattered pattern.

Writing poems needs time
To play around with the sounds of words,
And colour the picture in your mind
Just because it's half past two
And Monday afternoon,
Doesn't mean I can write a poem.

Home at last,
Lying on the grass,
Prickly and hot,
Watching a beetle
Struggle through the maze,
A butterfly danced through the flowers
Pausing at every one.
Its wings like
Bits of white paper
Thrown away.

I sometimes wonder
How butterflies get back to their home,
Because they can't fly straight
Just like my thoughts
Looking for somewhere to rest.

Kirsten MacDonald-Bennett (11)

Samantha West (15)

REFUGE

She sat by the window,
Looking down at the children playing in the street,
She longed to join them,
To be one of the 'gang'.
One looked up and saw her at the window,
He pointed at her, laughing, jeering.
Tears stung her eyes
And she returned to her wonder world
In the land of literature.

She was a Greek warrior now.
A bright tunic and leather sandals
Replaced her dirty jeans and baseball boots.
She was at Knossos,
Winter palace of the Cretan Kings.
She watched the bull dancers
Flinging themselves at the bulls,
Somersaulting over their horns.
She wondered at their agility
And marvelled at their bravery.
Now she joined them.
Her supple body leaping skywards
Over the bull's broad back,
Doing handstands on the bloodstained horns
Where many a boastful bull dancer
Met their death,
But not she.
Cheers rose and rapturous applause awarded her
As she jumped, spun and flipped
To dodge the diving horns.
The bull charged,

She leapt and landed on its back.
The bull bucked and she soared high,
High into the air.
She glided, feeling the fresh air on her face.
The warm sun on her back,
She breathed in deeply,
The stinging aroma of salty sea filled her lungs,
And she flew on.
Now under her
There was a great ship.
Wooden timbers creaking
As it gently rocked from side to side.
A gentle puff of air
Brought her slowly to the solid deck.
A crack of a whip
Startled her, she jumped up.
Her ears ached to the groan of sweating men
Heaving on the heavy oars.
She winced at the pungent smell
Of sweat, rotting food and sea.
She looked up at the blinding sun,
The wispy, thin clouds.
And, once more, tears pricked her eyes.

She looked up.
Down in the street there was silence.
A small gust of wind
Caught an empty crisp packet
And tossed it into the air.
A Coke can rattled noisily
As it rolled down the street.
And the smell of Sunday lunch
Dragged her downstairs.
Away from her books.

Ann Dugan (9)

LAST NIGHT I DIED

Last night I died and went to heaven. It was misted and cold looking. I walked up to Jesus. He was sitting on a very big seat. He looked very cold. He had the holes on his hands like my mummy said he would. He said in a low voice,

'Welcome.'

I said,

'Thank you.'

I went all round heaven. I met friends. Everyone was very nice to me. That night Jesus showed me to my room and I had a dream about home.

** HENRY THE NAVIGATOR

Mrs Avery picked up the salt shaker and drifted into the kitchen. She looked around, absently wondering what it was that she had come in to do. Then, replacing the shaker in its position behind the egg-wheel, she went back into the breakfast room where her husband was clearing the rest of the crockery on to a green checkerboard tray. Clearing was his job. Clearing, baking fruit tarts to be frozen for when the cousins came, vacuuming, dusting, polishing and fixing the aerial on the television set when it toppled at sudden, alarming intervals. Her jobs were, on the other hand, shopping, ironing (the only woman on Ellbogarde Street West who ironed underpants), following the diets that her husband planned out in blue letters for her, and, of course, the salt shaker and pepper mill, which she dutifully replaced after each meal. Egg-wheel; salt; coffee pot; pepper. It was one of the rituals. Afterwards, she'd cluck out of the kitchen like a satisfied hen.

'All right, dear?' said Henry, shadow-slinking past her with the tray. Mrs Avery, Mrs Ruth-Ann Sacramento Avery, nodded and sat. She could hear him chink the tray down and pad back to his armchair. He picked up a book. Science. If there was one thing Mrs Ruth-Ann Sacramento Avery could not stand it was books. Especially when they were read by a buttermint-scrunching Henry.

He, for his part, had learned long ago that his wife had no interest in the ideas that whizzed and swooped and swan-dived into the peach-flesh hollows of his head. Before they were married, he'd invented a few things; not twentieth-century startlers that would guarantee his name a place in the history books, but toys, that buzzed or chimed or whirled around the floor on piston-pump legs.

One time he'd presented a sticky niece, who had been sporting an arresting and brilliant cherryade moustache, with a foot-long dragon who snorted real smoke from its flared nostrils. The niece, however, saved any amusement she may have felt for the display until the moment it guttered and snarled from inside its belly, and then gulfed out scorchy yellow flames which set the carpet alight.

No, Mrs Avery did not like it at all. She refused to listen when he tried to tell her about the genius of Humphry Davy, or Frank Whittle, and she was perfectly happy in the knowledge that she would never, ever see Jodrell Bank, whatever it was, even out of the window of a locked-up car on a rainy Saturday afternoon. The truth was, science, and knowledge, and learning, and men who lounged for hours among plipping plopping Doctor Jekyll test tubes made her so uncomfortable that she'd have to lock herself in the bathroom and read the backs of shampoo bottles and skin preparations until the whole mess of them disappeared, canary-quick, from her mind.

Henry flipped over a page with a rustle dry as snakeskin. The radio cracked and whittered under her fingers, snapping a previously dormant funeral march to life. She sat back in her chair and stared around the room. The two peacock-coloured chinamen with their cat's faces and cat's paws glared down from the top shelf. Henry had bought them. A trip to China, or India, or someplace out East. She closed her eyes. 'Trick, trick.' It had rained for a full week. Girls in the street slushpuddled with their feet, while the bus, miles away, surged in a titanic froth of gutter water.

Henry sighed to himself and wiped his forehead with his open book, leaving a dull smudge. He put the book down. He took off his glasses. He leaned back and closed his eyes, willing the funeral march, or the rain, or his wife's breathing, to waft into his brain, through his ear, and wash away the thoughts that were coiling, taut, like angry copper springs. Cogs, springs, nuts and bolts. 'God damn you!' thought Henry angrily. 'Get out!' He was beginning to sweat a little; the fire was very hot; the music seemed to have become louder and more distant all at once. 'BACH, Johann Sebastian,' said Henry's head. 'German composer. Church Cantatas. Passions. 1685– 1750.' Henry leapt up, agonised. It was happening again.

Once inside the kitchen, he began to fill the bowl with soapy water and started to scrape the remains of dinner into the dustbin. Frying made such a mess of the pans, he thought absently. The storm was beginning to die down. He felt his armpits damp with relief.

'BACON, FRANCIS. BACON, ROGER. SCIENTISTS AND PHILOSOPHERS. ASTRONOMY! CHEMISTRY! OPTICS! ARISTOTLE!' The plates crashed to the floor and shattered into chunks. Henry pounded his head with his fists, flapping like a terrorised albatross, cramped in a too-small nest and bulging with dangerously hatching eggs. His wife appeared in the door frame.

'What happened?' she said.

Henry looked up at her, through a tangle of his own red sleeves, and then rather foolishly got up from his knees.

'I dropped a plate,' he said, 'or two.'

He struggled to hear Ruth-Ann through the screeching rumble that was bellowing inside his head. 'PLATO!' it shouted. 'GREEK PHILOSOPHER AND PUPIL OF SOCRATES! 427–347BC IDEAS! REFORMS! CALLIPOLIS!'

There was a silence. Through it, and faintly, he heard, 'Sweep that mess up before the cats get in.' His wife disappeared, leaving him naked on the battlefield.

'Not again, not again,' muttered Henry, broken. He couldn't risk that all over again, not now. Not after seventeen years of safety.

'What the hell am I going to do?' He stopped, with the ashpan in his hand; and outside the rain dripped. 'Trick, trick, trick.'

He had to get out of the kitchen. He could feel it starting:

'HORATIO HERBERT! 1850–1916! YOUR COUNTRY NEEDS YOU!' Mrs Avery looked up. Henry had appeared in the room very suddenly, with a deep sound that seemed to have originated somewhere in his belly. She sat up. 'Henry, what is it with you? Will you please calm down! You're making me jumpy.'

'You're jumpy?' thought Henry dismally. 'Sweet Jesus.' He sat down.

'In fact,' said Ruth-Ann, 'I think I'll turn in. You coming?'

'No,' said Henry. 'I think I'll just sit awhile. I'll be in later.'

His wife squinted at him. 'Well, don't make too much noise when you do. Goodnight.' She closed the door behind her. 'Really,' she thought. 'And he's been so quiet all day.'

Meanwhile, Henry was pacing in circles. He had been surprised by a sudden and vicious attack from Confucius, 551–479, and was presently engaged in the gloomily futile attempt to shake him, slant-eyed and thinking deeply, from where he appeared to be sitting, just at the back of his head. Then he stopped. He heard the tap water gurgle down the drain, he heard his wife close the bathroom door, close the bedroom door, and he heard the old bed sag like a pregnant cow-belly under her weight. The house was unnervingly quiet. Henry put on his socks. Maybe the cold wet air would dampen him. He knew the danger signs. He must not, on any account, go near the cellar, and he could feel his feet beginning to estrange themselves from his bodily will and show the first signs of dragging him places he didn't want to go. He put on an old pair of track shoes and silently went out the front door. It was late. The street lay before him, glistening in the pale orange light that floated hot and wet in rivulets over the road. He began to run. Puffing a little, he set his face, determined. This should do the trick.

'Trick, trick, trick.'

'Thomas Alva Edison,' said a tiny voice. 'Maxr Planck.' Henry gathered speed. He was very hot. The voice was not coming from his head any more. With mounting horror he saw the words, as if etched in flame appear like sirens across his chest. 'IVAN PAVLOV 1849–1936!' Henry was almost roaring with desperation. He pulled off his sweater and flung it into the air, still running. He could hear it hiss and fizzle out in one of the sidewalk lakes. His legs were aching. 'POMPEY THE GREAT!' said his left. 'MARCO POLO!' said his right. Henry rocketed into a gateway and tugged furiously at his brown slacks. He had a hard time getting them over his track shoes, and his hands, covered with wet, black grains from the soles, were not working at their best.

He set off again, a fat, white, old man dressed only in his shoes and his underpants. He panted and puffed, freezing, and feeling his soft belly shake with exertion. 'Why me?' he thought in desperation. He had run around the block and was almost back at his front door. By now his underpants were sodden and heavy at his ankles. He stepped out of them, leaving them ominous at the gate. Perhaps by morning they would have floated away. He couldn't pick them up now, not with the voice that bellowed from their elastic. Ruth-Ann was sleeping. Henry, naked but for his running shoes and socks, closed the front door behind him. He was filthy. There was nothing he could do now. The cellar gaped in seductive invitation. Grabbing his wife's brown coat from the hatstand as his feet shuttled him down the hall, he was shunted into the cellar door, which, in his rude state, was not surprisingly uncomfortable. Once inside the cellar and down the steps, Henry knew there was no turning back. Wildly, he thought of the post-retirement job he had secured for next week, how he had planned to work efficiently, take a salad with him for his lunch, drink coffee with the girls from the typing pool.

There was no place for that now.

Lifting the heavy cover from his invention, he paused. He thought of the hospital. Seventeen years had not subdued the horror of that. It was, though, a risk he would just have to take. Maybe by the time Ruth-Ann telephoned the authorities he would be far enough away for them to sigh and cross him off their books as a lost cause. He put on the coat, which bristled against his bare flesh, and clambered into his flying machine. The voice was booming now, coming from somewhere so profound Henry's ears almost curled up and fluttered like butterflies in colourful spirals towards its source. Surely his wife, safe in her bed, could hear it. Surely the hospital, forty miles away and forbiddingly shiny could hear it. Or was Henry the Enlightened One, smalltime white Buddha in his wife's old coat, specifically chosen for the most important Siddharta flight yet? The machine was buzzing now, ready to fly. Henry the Navigator Mark Two, AVERY, HENRY THE NAVIGATOR, born 1912 and still, if rather cold, bulging with life, set about the dials and gauges.

It had taken him a long time to build. The plans had begun to ferment in his mind even while he was at the hospital, surrounded by the chalkfaced soup-slurpers, and the wounded soldiers who wept when their empty plates were collected. Once home again, he had prudently decided to leave well alone, but after a few months, he found himself collecting, as he had done before, the springs and tacks and engines necessary for his final tribute to his love. He felt his temples swell with it, he could taste science on his breath, feel it in his fingertips. Oh, if Brunel could see him now! Henry was sure he could, they all could. And soon he would join them in Callipolis. When he arrived, he would greet Lao-Tzu with a weary smile. Henry the Navigator has not lost his way.

'Praise God. Praise Jesus!' roared Henry, as the machine rose heavy into the air and up the cellar steps. A splintering crash disposed of the door that had been in his way, a glassy one shattered as he left the house behind. He was free, seventy-six and rising high. As he looked down at the snaking blocks of the city, he was sure he heard his wife turn peacefully over in her sleep. Even forty miles up, naked, Henry heard her slice through his joy. Settling back into the comfortable pilot seat that had once been a kitchen chair, Henry held his chin in his hands and smiled. Even if I don't make the journey, he thought to himself, even if I don't arrive, it may well still be worth it.

And the wrinkled picture in his mind, a crowd of people standing in a ring, with Henry in the centre surrounded by pieces of his plane, exhausted, but best of all, with his wife's coat flapping around his legs, became smooth and solid, even through the trick trick dripping of the November rain.

David Hurley (8)

DYSLEXIA

The words on the page get all muddled up,
The word I try to read is all squashed together.
Small writing is the worst,
'Prince Caspian' becomes 'Pince Caspen'.
The words run around my head,
My head makes it very hard to know what they said.
To see all the others doing it right,
Makes it hard to see it right,
And all sorts of funny things go running through my
    head.
The words aren't really anywhere,
They're somewhere else instead.

Rupert Privett (12)

Andrew Pierson (8)

*   **SEAGULLS**

The playground is noisy and full of bustle. As the bell is
    about to ring.
The herring gulls begin to circle overhead.
When the playground is clear.
The scavengers swoop down.
They squawk and squabble.
They strut and waddle about
Stabbing at the ground with
Scissored beak for tasty morsels.
They look very comical with their heads nodding up and
    down as they parade along.
They call each other with a high-pitched sad plaintive
    sorrowful sound that reminds me of long gone
    holidays.

Emma Imison (8)

I AM A ROUNDABOUT HORSE

I am a roundabout horse. It is boring
going round and round. With children
pulling my mane and kicking
their heels into me. It is horrid
seeing the backs of the horse in
front. And the same music every
day.

Sinead Wilson (15)

*   **OUT OF THE RAIN**

Wet devils
  can dance in mackintoshes
      in the rain
   licking the pavements dry
     with their hot little tongues
But I
  shall stay here
cosy in the womb of my sofa
  remembering
how dust plays in the sunlight
  which comes trooping in
     with a sigh
    like a silent curtain.

INDEX

* Award-winners
** Special Award-winners
Illustrators

* **Abrahams,** Ben	Whalley CE Primary School, Blackburn	130
Alizadeh, Saranaz	*St James's Independent School for Girls, London SW7*	*180*
Allen, Trudy	Swanage Middle School, Dorset	177
* **Banerjee,** Bikiron	St Dunstan's College, London SE6	112
* **Barnes,** Michelle	Halesworth Middle School, Suffolk	35, 52
** **Beckinsale,** Kate	Godolphin and Latymer School, London W6	77, 114, 193
Beresford, Lorraine	Whalley CE Primary School, Blackburn	46
* **Berry,** Katherine	Presentation of Mary Convent School, Exeter	28
Bertrand, Christopher	*Halesworth Middle School, Suffolk*	*183*
* **Billinge,** Kate	Altrincham Grammar School for Girls, Cheshire	25
Binder, Joe	*Halesworth Middle School, Suffolk*	*139*
Bird, *Tammy*	*Halesworth Middle School, Suffolk*	*21*
Brandram, *Sophie*	*Garden House School, London SW3*	*12*
Broderick, Clare	Gossy Lane School, Birmingham	46, 178
* **Brown,** Evan	Uig Primary School, Isle of Skye	53, 53
Bryant, *Freddie*	*Halesworth Middle School, Suffolk*	*67*
* **Buckingham,** Emma	Halesworth Middle School, Suffolk	43, 142
Chaudry, Maimuna	GWC, Edinburgh	26
Clarke, Catherine	Parkstone Grammar School, Poole, Dorset	44, 45
Clements, Victoria	Nativity School, Sittingbourne, Kent	42
Colvert, Richard	Westcliff High School for Boys, Essex	163
Davies, Lorna	*Chelmsford County High School for Girls, Essex*	*55*
Davis, Kate	*Garden House School, London SW3*	*95*

Dearsley, Thomas   *Godalming County Middle School, Surrey*   *109*

Devonald, Emma   *St Martin's Infants' School, Salisbury*   107

Dickerson, Sophie   *Garden House School, London SW3*   177

Downes, Gary   *Halesworth Middle School, Suffolk*   136

Drewe, Nadav   UCS (Junior Branch), London NW3   140

Dugan, Ann   St Patrick's Primary School, Armagh   192

Earis, Harriet   Godalming County Middle School, Surrey   129

* **Echlin**, Helena   The Henrietta Barnet School, London NW11   111, 180

* **Edwards**, Hannah   Halesworth Middle School, Suffolk   36, 39, 137

Ellis, Tom   *The King's School, Canterbury*   *88, 171*

Felcey, Helen   *Whalley CE Primary School, Blackburn*   *47, 161*

Ferley, Dylan   *Whalley CE Primary School, Blackburn*   *87*

Fleming, Justin   *Shaftesbury Upper School, Dorset*   *96*

Forbes, Euan   *Godalming County Middle School, Surrey*   *129*

** **Gardam**, Stephen   Halesworth Middle School, Suffolk   40, 62, 63, 149

* **Garvey**, Una   Mount St Catherine's Primary School, Armagh   106

* **Goodwin**, Gavin   Halesworth Middle School, Suffolk   22

Gordon-Lennox, Simon   *Highfield School, Liphook, Hampshire*   *133*

* **Graham**, Anthony   St Patrick's Primary School, Armagh   58

Hambling, James   *Halesworth Middle School, Suffolk*   *9*

Hawker, Katherine   Groby Community College, Leicestershire   150

Haworth, Anya   *Whalley CE Primary School, Blackburn*   *69*

Holt, Andrew   River County Primary, Dover   148

* **Howden**, John   Prestbury CE (Aided) Primary School, Cheshire   85

Hucker, Georgina   *Halesworth Middle School, Suffolk*   *24*

Hudson, Elisa   *The King's School, Canterbury*   *49*

Hurley, David   Highfield School, Liphook, Hampshire   200

** **Huston**, Avril   Chelmsford County High School for Girls, Essex   54, 164, 186

Idle, Emma   *Halesworth Middle School, Suffolk*   *125*

Imison, Emma   Prestbury C of E Primary School (Aided), Cheshire   203

Jarvis, Simon   *Whalley CE Primary School, Blackburn*   *61, 141*

*	**Khan,** Bilquees	St James's Independent School for Girls, London SW7	31, 51
*	**Lewis,** Miriam	Grove Road Junior School, Rayleigh, Essex	13
	Line, Edward	Halesworth Middle School, Suffolk	60
	Luke, Victoria	*Halesworth Middle School, Suffolk*	*105*
	MacDonald-Bennett, Kirsten	*Highfield School, Liphook, Hampshire*	*189*
	Mair, William	Halesworth Middle School, Suffolk	138
	Malin, Keith	Foulds School, Barnet, Herts	185
	Mason, Nichola	*Halesworth Middle School, Suffolk*	*37*
	McCarthy, Craig	*Whalley CE Primary School, Blackburn*	*127*
	McCrory, Katie-Ellen	St Martin's Infants' School, Salisbury	19
*	**McNaught,** Andrew	The King's School, Canterbury	89
	Mercer, Stephen	St Olave's Grammar School, Orpington, Kent	124
*	**Mitchell,** Anna	Loddington CE Primary School, Kettering, Northants	86
	Mitchell, James	Loddington CE Primary School, Kettering, Northants	188
*	**Mitchell,** Matilda	The King's School, Canterbury	170
	Noller, Louise	*Halesworth Middle School, Suffolk*	*42*
*	**Pattle,** Christopher	Eynesbury CE Primary School, Huntingdon, Cambs	132
*	**Payton,** Ryan	Eynesbury CE Primary School, Huntingdon, Cambs	33
*	**Pierson,** Andrew	Lincewood Junior School, Basildon, Essex	202
	Pike, Jamie	*Halesworth Middle School, Suffolk*	*123*
	Plentl, Marina	Garden House School, London SW3	21, 59
	Powell-Evans, Gareth	*Halesworth Middle School, Suffolk*	*39*
	Privett, Rupert	*Highfield School, Liphook, Hampshire*	*201*
*	**Prochnik,** Rebecca	James Allen's Girls' School, London SE22	56
	Rawlings, Alison	*Halesworth Middle School, Suffolk*	*75*
	Richardson, Seth	*St Martin's Infants' School, Salisbury*	*18*
	Rickard, Sophie	*Whalley CE Primary School, Blackburn*	*166*
	Roach, William	*St Martin's Infants' School, Salisbury*	*18, 19*
	Robinson, Philip	St John's RC Comprehensive School, Co. Durham	70
	Routledge, Stephen	Rhydypenau School, Llanishen, Cardiff	176

* **Rubins,** Anna	The Latymer School, London N9	143
Rust, Marilyn	*Halesworth Middle School, Suffolk*	23
Ryan, Rebecca	*Whalley CE Primary School, Blackburn*	131
Savat-Manesh,		
Samannaz	*Garden House School, London SW3*	20
Saxey, Esther	Shaftesbury Upper School, Dorset	97
Scriven, Samantha	*Halesworth Middle School, Suffolk*	136
* **Semple,** Helen	James Allen's Girls' School, London SE22	64
Seneviratne,	*St James's Independent School for Girls,*	
Anoushka	*London SW7*	51
Shearn, Nick	*Shaftesbury Upper School, Dorset*	100
Sinclair, Elizabeth	St Helen's School, Northwood, Middlesex	90
Sizer, Lucy	*Chelmsford County High School for Girls,*	
	Essex	117
* **Smith-Hayes,** Marnie	Halesworth Middle School, Suffolk	135
Sparrow, Helen	*St Martin's Infants' School, Salisbury*	178
* **Starkey,** Ashley	Rednock School, Dursley, Glos	84
* **Steele-Perkins,** Emma	Port Regis School, Dorset	20
Taylor, Adam	*St Martin's Infants' School, Salisbury*	27
* **Taylor,** Amy	Highfield School, Liphook, Hampshire	105
Thomas, Sacha	Avenue Infant School, Leicester	38
Thompson, Nicola	*Whalley CE Primary School, Blackburn*	169
Timson, Catherine	*Whalley CE Primary School, Blackburn*	103
* **Tyler,** Joanna	Halesworth Middle School, Suffolk	24
Walter, Karen	*Halesworth Middle School, Suffolk*	52
Ward, Natalie	*Halesworth Middle School, Suffolk*	41
West, Samantha	Tonbridge Grammar School, Kent	190
Westell, John	*Whalley CE Primary School, Blackburn*	83
Wharf, Lydia	Pates Grammar School, Cheltenham, Glos	172
White, Susie	*Chelmsford County High School for Girls,*	
	Essex	187
* **Wilson,** Sinead	Godolphin and Latymer School,	
	London W6	179, 204
Woolston, Neil	*Halesworth Middle School, Suffolk*	34
Wright, Charlotte	Belsize Park, London NW3	175
Yaqoob, Ansar	Drummond Road Middle School, Bradford	11